CONFIRMATION AND CONFIRMABILITY

G. SCHLESINGER

Confirmation
and
Confirmability

CLARENDON PRESS · OXFORD
1974

Oxford University Press, Ely House, London W. 1

GLASGOW NEW YORK TORONTO MELBOURNE WELLINGTON
CAPE TOWN IBADAN NAIROBI DAR ES SALAAM LUSAKA ADDIS ABABA
DELHI BOMBAY CALCUTTA MADRAS KARACHI LAHORE DACCA
KUALA LUMPUR SINGAPORE HONG KONG TOKYO

ISBN 0 19 824511 4

© Oxford University Press 1974

Printed in Great Britain
by J. W. Arrowsmith Ltd., Bristol

Acknowledgements

Many of the ideas developed in this book have germinated elsewhere, e.g. *Analysis, American Philosophical Quarterly, Boston Studies in the Philosophy of Science, Journal of Philosophy, Nous, Philosophical Quarterly.* I wish to thank the respective editors for having permitted me to use the pages of their journals from where to launch these ideas.

Parts of this book have been written while I was a recipient of a N.S.F. Grant.

I should like to take this opportunity to record my indebtedness to Brian Ellis from whom I have learnt more than from anyone else.

I should also like to thank my friend Tom Morris for helping me with proof reading and preparing an index.

Contents

Introduction

Teaching the philosophy of science can be a most rewarding experience. Students can with little technical preparation be introduced to a series of unexpected and exciting results. The handling of most of the really interesting issues requires neither thorough acquaintance with all the latest results of science nor advanced mathematical skill. The intelligent student is quick to respond when the topic is presented to him in the proper way and soon acquires the knack of tackling the issues discussed by the practitioners of the discipline.

The material in this book and the method of presentation are based on my experience of teaching over the last decade. Inevitably, therefore, the reader will sense that much of what is presented and especially the manner in which it is presented is governed by pedagogical considerations. Indeed, I have written this book in the hope that, whether or not it is used as a whole, its major usefulness will lie in a capacity to provoke students into creative thinking about problems in the philosophy of science.

We begin with confirmation of the most simple kind, employed mainly in prescientific, commonsense reasoning, and at once we find ourselves faced with paradoxes. It does not take long to realize that even the most elementary form of empirical reasoning is beset with problems as a result of the fact that no generalization is made in a vacuum and all true propositions are part of a large intermeshing system of knowledge claims.

In the second chapter we deal with H. Jeffreys's famous problem that a finite set of experimental results can always be equally well accounted for by an infinite number of hypotheses, thus causing us to wonder how we are to pick the 'right' one among these hypotheses. This tantalizing problem which affects in the same way all the results of science, is modified so as to make some of the suggested solutions—

including Jeffreys's own—irrelevant. In my experience it is one of those rare problems in philosophy which can arouse keen interest in the ordinary scientist, who, as a rule, is impatient with abstract analysis of scientific method.

I attempt to show that in general, faced with the problem of there being infinitely many available hypotheses, we end up choosing the one which we do choose not because we have reason to believe it is the most likely to be true but because the methodological rule we have adopted picks it out from among all the others. Now the methodological rule we have adopted is not merely superior in this or that respect to its rivals, it *has* no rivals. It is the only rule which when employed by different people, in a wide variety of circumstances, will yield the same results.

Subsequently, an outline of a solution to the problem of induction is advanced. The suggestion does not advocate the kind of solution that is known either as a 'justification' or as a 'vindication' of induction. That is, it is neither claimed that there is any guarantee that the inductive method will yield or is likely to yield correct results nor that at least, if any method will yield correct results, then so will induction. The prevailing scientific method is defended by arguing that, if it may be presupposed that what we want is a method of predicting the future which will make maximum use of past observations, then there just is no other method than the one actually used in science.

In the third chapter a definition of confirmation is sought. We find that knowing all the available evidence is not sufficient to determine whether a given hypothesis is confirmed to any degree. It is necessary to know also all the alternative theories that can account in various ways for the same set of observations which serves as our evidence. The fact that a hypothesis is strongly confirmed relative to a given theory furnishes no assurance whatever that it is confirmed in an absolute sense. It is easily shown that every hypothesis is confirmed relative to some theory. But only when the theory relative to which a hypothesis is confirmed is the most acceptable among its rivals is the hypothesis to be regarded as confirmed in an absolute sense.

At this stage we move on to consider the question of what might serve as an adequate criterion of confirmability (or verifiability) in principle by which to distinguish between sentences that are empirically significant and those that are not. When teaching the subject, it has been my practice to survey the history of verificationism and examine the various significant attempts to set up such a criterion. The more one studies the failures of past attempts, the more one tends to believe the whole enterprise to be hopeless. Yet, when one begins, as we do here, to investigate the question of empirical significance after setting up a criterion for the credibility of empirical statements, that is, after one has constructed a criterion to determine what is actually confirmed, the problem of determining what is confirmable in principle no longer looks insoluble at all. Once it is appreciated that the confirmation of hypotheses is a two-staged affair, a natural way to escape the difficulties which beset verificationism suggests itself: confirmability in principle is a two-stage process also. It matters not that it can be shown that any statement is confirmable relative to some theory; empirical significance attaches only to those statements which can be shown to be confirmable relative to theories which, under some logically possible circumstances, would be regarded as the most acceptable ones.

In the fourth chapter the scope of the principle which underlies the confirmability criterion of empirical significance is widened and shown also to underlie considerations that lead us to declare certain sentences which gave rise to paradoxes as meaningless. Here, for the only time, we use very briefly some elementary techniques of symbolic logic. It need not worry readers unacquainted with these, since the drift of the arguments can be fully grasped from the non-technical parts of the text. In the light of the explanation given in this chapter, that the criterion of confirmability follows from a very general and obviously reasonable principle, the criterion need no longer be associated with the special ideology of logical posivitism and should be acceptable at all.

The usefulness of a viable confirmability criterion is not confined to the reconfirmation of the meaningfulness or meaninglessness of sentences we already know to possess or lack meaning respectively. The criterion may be shown to be a useful tool in investigating the status of hypotheses whose significance is truly in question. At the same time it is not the case that, now that we are in possession of a criterion, the application of it is a routine procedure. Careful reasoning is required in order to reach a plausible conclusion on the status of sentences, the significance of which is genuinely in doubt. The last two chapters are devoted to demonstrating how indeed one is to apply the criterion in concrete instances. While in chapter five we consider the confirmability of a first-order scientific statement, in chapter six we deal with a second-order statement. First-order statements describe how nature is and second-order statements make claims about first-order statements; that is, while first-order statements are about natural phenomena, second-order statements are about natural science.

I recognize that a number of views are advanced in this book which will probably not pass undisputed. To mention some of the important points that are most likely to arouse scepticism, I claim, in spite of all that has been written about the insolubility of the problem of induction or the lack of need to solve it, that I have presented what amounts in a certain sense to a solution; that, in spite of the successive failures in the last few decades to construct a confirmability criterion of empirical significance, I have constructed such a criterion which should be generally acceptable and is at the same time useful and interesting; and (in the last chapter) that, while the assertion that the world is fully deterministic is confirmable in principle, the denial of this claim has neither been confirmed in fact nor is it conceivable that is should ever be so confirmed.

But as I said in the beginning, I have written this book in the hope that it will be found to contain useful material with which to stimulate discussion. As such, the absolute validity of everything I say in it is not of essential importance. Needless to say, however, while I recognize that what follows does not contain the whole truth and perhaps not even only the truth, I hope it contains enough of the truth to stimulate some readers to want to refine some of the main arguments and to develop further the major contentions, thus leading to a greater understanding of the subject.

In conclusion let me say that the most important point, which is not explicitly made in the book but is only implied by its approach, a point I am most anxious to make, is that it may still be worthwhile to attempt to make a contribution to the philosophy of science by writing without filling the pages with symbols and in such a manner that the result should be accessible to a reasonably patient intelligent reader who is not trained in advanced mathematics.

CHAPTER I   The Confirmation
of Simple
Generalizations

(1) *Nicod's Criterion*

We shall begin our study of the ways in which evidence is related to
hypotheses by considering the most simple type of generalization of
the form 'All P's are Q's', that is, every individual characterized as P
has the property Q[e.g. 'All ravens are black' where for P we have
raven and for Q black and where blackness is not taken as a defining
characteristic of ravenness] . Such generalizations are found mainly in
elementary science or commonsense, prescientific reasoning. It would
seem that an individual which had both the properties P and Q confirmed, one which had P but not Q disconfirmed, and one which did
not have P was neutral to, the empirical generalization 'All P's are Q's'.
Indeed, what has been just said is known as the Nicod criterion of
confirmation which has been summarized by Hempel thus: 'If h is a
hypothesis of universal conditional form and contains one-place predicates only, then h is confirmed by any object that satisfies both its
antecedent and its consequent; and h is disconfirmed by any object
that satisfies its antecedent but not its consequent.'[1] In symbols:
(a) An observational report Pi & Qi [i.e. individual i has both the
property P and the property Q] confirms $(x) (P \supset Qx)$ [i.e. 'for
every x, if x is a raven then x is black']
(b) an observational report Pi & $\sim Qi$ disconfirms the same and
(c) observational reports $\sim Pi$ & Qi, $\sim Pi$ & $\sim Qi$ are neutral to the
generalization.
It should be noted that (b) requires no justification, since given
that the generalization is incompatible with observation it stands to

[1] *Boston Studies in the Philosophy of Science,* ii. (1965) p. 19. Note that
the term 'confirmed' is employed here in a weak sense and stands for 'received
some empirical support' and not for 'conclusively verified', whereas 'disconfirmed' is used in a strong sense meaning 'refuted'.

reason that the generalization has to be withdrawn. As to (a) and (c) no justification is being offered. Nicod's criterion is merely meant to be a simple articulation of what in the elementary situation referred to is commonsensically regarded as supporting evidence and what is not.

(2) *Hempel's Paradox*

It becomes evident very soon why it is so instructive to begin our studies with Nicod's criteria (a), (b), and (c). They concern the most elementary form of empirical reasoning and seem to express simple and generally agreed truth. And yet with a minimum amount of logical analysis it is shown not merely that (a), (b), and (c) happen to be false but that they form an inconsistent set of propositions and their conjunction is therefore logically false. This has been demonstrated by Hempel through the proposal of a famous paradox which bears his name.

'All ravens are black' is logically equivalent to 'All non-black things are non-ravens'. Everything confirming one confirms to exactly the same extent the other (for it would be logically absurd to claim that while *p* is confirmed to such and such degree, *q*, its logical equivalent, is slightly more or slightly less confirmed). But by Nicod's (a) the second generalization is confirmed by a non-black individual which is also a non-raven, e.g. a white shoe. Thus the observation of a white shoe confirms that all ravens are black contrary to Nicod's (c). Thus Nicod's (a) implies the denial of his criterion (c). At the same time, the conclusion that a white shoe indeed confirms 'All ravens are black', to any degree, is strongly counter-intuitive.

Hempel's own radical solution consists in rejecting Nicod's criterion (c) and in insisting that we have to abide by logical analysis, no matter how odd its results may seem to untutored common sense. He declares '. . . the impression of paradoxicality arises from a misguided intuition in the matter.'[1]

Many people have found this solution unpalatable and have refused to go along with the idea that there is really nothing strange in claiming that the observation of a white shoe counts as support to the generalization 'All ravens are black'.

[1] *Mind*, liv, 1946, p. 79.

G. H. von Wright has come forward with what may be regarded as a compromise solution.[1] He does not go as far as Hempel and he makes some concession to common sense. The central point of his suggestion is that the essence of confirmation does not consist in instantiating a generalization but rather in a generalization's being exposed to falsification, and successfully surviving the exposure. Thus, when an individual, which potentially constitutes a threat to a hypothesis turns out not to falsify it, then it leads the hypothesis confirmation by virtue of its failure to falsify. An individual which has never presented a threat to the hypothesis can provide no support for it.

In this spirit von Wright points out that not under all circumstances does it go against common sense to regard the observation of a white shoe as confirming 'All ravens are black'. It all depends on how we come to know that the object in front of us is a white shoe. If the first thing that came to our notice was its colour, then at that stage it presented a threat to our hypothesis since the possibility of its being a white raven had not then been ruled out. Upon subsequent verification, finding that is is not a raven, we may truly say that we have a genuine confirming instance of the law, since, through the observed object turning out to be a shoe, the law has stood the test and been saved from falsification. It is only if we first found that it was a shoe, but discovered afterwards that its colour was white, that it would be paradoxical to regard it as providing confirmation for our hypothesis since the object in question at no stage presented a possible threat to it. But then von Wright points out that there is complete symmetry here because the observation of a black raven too confirms the law only if its ravenness came to our attention before its blackness but not if its blackness was the first thing we discovered about it, since in that case it never constituted a possible source of falsification.

It would be incorrect to say that von Wright lays himself open to the accusation that he has introduced psychological or subjective considerations in the logic of confirmation. After all, when the observation of blackness had preceded that of ravenness, we have an objectively different observation from the one in which the order is reversed. But what one may wonder is whether indeed we do pay much attention to the order in which the observation of the properties

[1] *The Logical Problem of Induction,* Oxford, 1957, pp. 122–7.

of the relevant individuals is made. It seems quite clear that, as long as it is not known that anyone has observed a non-black raven and it is known that a considerable number of black ravens have been observed, we regard the generalization 'All ravens are black' as confirmed and we do not in the least feel the need to inquire in what manner these observations have taken place.

Von Wright could cope with this question without necessarily abandoning his claim that the confirmation of hypothesis consists in a potentially falsifying instance turning out compatible with it. When we are about to observe an object of which as yet we know nothing, it presents a threat to our hypothesis since it may turn out to be a non-black raven. For this reason, the mere observation of a black raven, irrespective of the order in which its ravenness and blackness have been observed, constitutes a confirming instance. But then, of course, for precisely the same reason the observation of a white shoe must, under all circumstances, provide confirmation for the same hypothesis—which we find unpalatable.

(3) *The Role of Background Knowledge*

I believe that the way our of our difficulties and to a generally better understanding of the nature of confirmation lies, first of all, in the realization that whether an observation b confirms a hypothesis h is not determined solely by the nature of b and its relation to h, but also by our presuppositions based partly on our previous observations and background knowledge constructed out of them.

To what extent factors extraneous to the report that an individual with the properties P and Q has been observed play a role in the confirmation of (x) $(Px \supset Qx)$ is best seen through considering some extreme examples in which these, and not such a report, seem the only factors that matter.

One group of examples is associated with situations in which not even a single i possessing both P and Q has been observed, yet the generalization is regarded as confirmed since it follows from theories we already subscribe to. Hempel[1] mentions two such examples. One concerns generalizations made by Mendeleev on the basis of his

[1] Op. Cit., p. 23.

periodic table with respect to the properties of elements which have, at the time, not yet been observed. Another of his examples refers to generalizations made about the behaviour of artificial satellites long before any of these has been launched and hence observed. That (x) $(Px \supset Qx)$ is confirmed where 'P' = 'is a projectile launched with initial velocity u' and 'Q' = 'will escape the Earth's gravitational pull' or where 'P' = 'has velocity v having an inclination of angle O to the direction of the moon' and 'Q' = 'will achieve lunar orbit' and so on has been established on the basis of Newton's laws of motion and before a single report of 'Pi & Qi' has been received.

There are even cases in which (x) $(Px \supset Qx)$ is accepted as strongly confirmed although neither has a report 'Pi & Qi' been received nor is it possible that such a report should ever be received. Generalizations made about the behaviour of samples of an ideal gas which is a physically impossible substance but whose essential properties have been ascertained on the basis of kinetic theory, serve as illustrations of this.

To another group of examples belong those situations in which numerous instances of a generalization have been observed, yet we refuse to regard the generalization as confirmed to any degree. This happens when strong theoretical considerations provided by our background knowledge prevent us from giving credence to the generalizations.

Suppose a new metal were discovered and heated through all the temperatures at which all known metals have melted, without melting, We should then have many instances of the generalization that, at every temperature which the newly discovered metal will reach, it will fail to melt. Yet I think we shall keep on believing that at some temperature the metal will melt. On the basis of what we regard as well-established facts about the atomic structure of all metals, we should refuse to believe that this metal had no melting-point.

Or, again, suppose that over an extended period it turned out that, whenever a crystal-gazer claimed to have observed certain shadows in his crystal ball, on that day the Dow-Jones Industrials fell, we should refuse to regard it as confirmed that on every day such a report is received from the crystal-gazer the Dow-Jones Industrials fall. We should prefer to explain the past correlation of the two events as a fraud to be eventually exposed or even as a highly unlikely coincidence. Our theoretical presuppositions do not permit us to believe in the possibility of a casual connection between the appearance of a crystal ball and the behaviour of the stock market. This, incidentally, brings out an important point, to be elaborated on later, that the reason why we believe that a generalization $(x) (Px \supset Qx)$ is true is because we think either that some cause resides in P which ensures the occurrence of Q or that there is some causal mechanism connecting $\sim Q$ to $\sim P$, or that there is a mechanism which produces both P and Q or $\sim Q$ and $\sim P$ from a common cause.

Finally, there are examples in which we have reports of 'Pi & $\sim Qi$' and yet we refuse to regard $(x) (Px \supset Qx)$ as disconfirmed. For example, occasional reports that the energy of a closed system has not been conserved have failed to shake the confidence of the scientific community in the First Law of Thermodynamics. In such cases, in which our belief in the truth of $(x) (Px \supset Qx)$ is too strong to be destroyed by a few reported counterexamples, the way we protect our hypothesis is by doubting the authenticity of the report.

The previous points are fairly well known. There are, however, other ways in which our presuppositions play a role in determining what effect an observation has on our theories: it is not the case that, simply by looking at an individual, we at once know enough about the conjunction of properties we have observed to support a generalization about the constant conjunction of a certain pair of properties. Background information, as we shall soon see, plays a crucial role in determining this for us.

(4) *Of the Many Classes an Individual Belongs to,*
      which does it represent?

Let us consider the generalization 'All swans are white' or in symbols

$$(x) (Sx \supset Wx) \qquad\qquad\qquad (g_1)$$

g_1 is logically equivalent to

$$(x) (\sim Wx \supset \sim Sx) \qquad\qquad\qquad (g'_1)$$

By Nicod's criterion (a) g'_1 should receive confirmation from an observational report '$\sim Wi$ & $\sim Si$', from a report stating that an individual i

was black (i.e. not white) and a raven (i.e. not a swan). Thus, since the observation of a black raven confirms g_1', and g_1' confirms g_1 which is its logical equivalent, the observation of a black raven confirms g_1.

Now, consider the generalization 'All birds are black', or in symbols

$$(x)\,(BDx{\supset}Bx) \tag{g_2}$$

By criterion (a) g_2 should be confirmed by a report '*BDi & Bi*' which would be based on the sighting of a black raven which is a black bird. The observation of a black raven therefore, supports, g_2. If it is to be assumed that at least one swan exists, then g_1 implies $\sim g_2$; that is, g_1 and g_2 are logically incompatible. Thus, criterion (a), which a moment ago looked as if it expressed an innocuous, commonly agreed truth, leads us to conclude that the observation of a black raven confirms inconsistent statements.

Let me state at once that I do not believe that the paradox we have just developed is a very disturbing one, but it will be instructive to find out just why it need not disturb us.

According to Hempel,[1] the crucial point is that g_1 alone does not entail $\sim g_2$, but does so only in conjunction with the extra empirical premises p (= swans exist) which happens to be true. In deriving the alleged paradox, I have employed the rule:

If b confirms g, and p is true and g and p entail h, then b confirms h. This rule, however, is not valid. The following consideration will show this at once: g and q together entail q, no matter what q stands for; hence, if the rule were valid, then b which confirmed g, would confirm also *any* arbitrary true statement q. This is clearly absurd.

It seems to me, however, that the paradox is not dissolved in the way Hempel suggests, for at least two reasons:

(1) Would not Hempel agree that if we were considering conclusive verification, rather than confirmation, then the following rule applied:

If b conclusively verifies g, and g and p together entail h and p is true, then b conclusively verifies h?

The answer, I am sure, is yes, provided the rule is supplemented by

---

[1] Op. cit., pp. 20–1.

saying 'given that *p* on its own does not entail *h*'. In a parallel fashion, the rule which is to be employed in deriving the paradox, a rule, which seems reasonable and valid until otherwise shown, is:

If *b* confirms *g*, and *p* is true and *g* jointly with *p* entails *h* while *p* on its own does not entail *h*, then *b* confirms *h*.

This rule, of course, does not permit *b* to confirm an arbitrary true statement *q* and has not, therefore, been shown to be absurd and invalid. But this restricted rule is sufficient for the derivation of the paradox.[1]

(2) But suppose even the revised rule is rejected for some reason. This would not lead to the dissolution of the paradox which may be derived without employing it.

Let '$R_2 i$' stand for 'the individual *i* is a raven at least two years old' and '$R_{-2} i$' stand for 'the individual *i* is a raven less than two years old'. The observation of a two-year-old black raven or the report '$R_2 i \,\&\, Bi$' confirms

$$(x)\,(\sim Wx \supset \sim R_{-2}x) \tag{g_3}$$

since the observed *i* is non-white and is not a raven less than two years old. But g_3 is equivalent to

$$(x)\,(R_{-2}x \supset Wx) \tag{g_3'}$$

and is confirmed by '$R_2 i \,\&\, Bi$'. In this case, we need no extra empirical premises that ravens less than two years old exist. From '$R_2 i$' alone it follows analytically that younger ravens, if not now, at least at some time in the past must have existed. Thus, '$R_2 i \,\&\, Bi$' which, of course, confirms 'All ravens are black' is now found to confirm the negation of this generalization since by g_3' all ravens less than two years old are non-black. '$R_2 i \,\&\, Bi$' confirms 'All ravens are black' as we have always assumed, but at the same time we find, to our surprise, it also confirms

---

[1] It may still seem that our rule is untenable for the following reason: Let *b* confirm *g* and let *g* be false, in which case $g \supset b$ must be true. Denote $g \supset b$ by *p* then by Modus Ponens $g \& p \rightarrowtail b$ and by our rule we are forced to concede that *b* confirms $\sim b$ whis is absurd.

The answer, however, is that in order to know that *p* is true it is necessary to know that *g* is false. But if *g* is known to be false then *b* does not confirm it on the reasonable principle that no observation confirms any hypothesis known to be false.

that *not* all ravens are black since by g_3' ravens less than two years old are all non-black.

It seems to me, however, that the paradox is simply avoided if we consider for a moment what is going on in actual empirical generalizations. Are 'All swans are white' and 'All birds are black' ever concurrently entertained as possible true generalizations? Surely not. As a general principle, we always assume the maximum uniformity compatible with observation. As long as only black birds have been observed, the observation of a black raven will be taken as confirming not merely 'All ravens are black' (and far less the even more restricted 'All ravens in the age group of this raven are black') but also the more general 'All birds are black' or 'g_2'. At this stage, therefore, the observed i does not confirm g_1 since it is not taken as confirming something about some species of birds but about all birds. After we had later observed non-black birds, the same i would serve as confirming g_1, but at that time it no longer confirms g_2. Thus while it may be that a given i is a candidate for confirming both g_1 and g_2 which are incompatible, at any given time it actually confirms only one of them, depending on the state of our knowledge at the time. Again, the same i may, at some time, be taken as confirming a hypothesis concerning ravens of a certain age group but only after some observation has forced us to abandon the assumption of uniformity among all ravens.

Every individual is a member of a great many classes. Which of the hypotheses, assigning a given property to all the members of a variety of classes, each including the individual possessing that property, is to be regarded as confirmed through an observation of the individual in question? Our individual i belongs to the class of two-year-old ravens, of ravens in general as well as the class of non-swans, of birds, of animals, and of material objects. In observing i to be black are we observing it as a member of the class of birds, of ravens, of non-swans, or of the innumerable other classes to which it belongs? It is obvious that this question cannot be decided by looking more closely or carefully at i and that some extra considerations have to be introduced. One of the extra considerations is that, of all the classes which are subclasses of one another, e.g. the class of two-year-old male ravens, of two-year-old ravens, of ravens, of birds, of animals, etc., we choose the most inclusive one as long as this is consistent with our background knowledge. Indeed, were it possible our i would serve as confirming 'All animals are black' but now it is taken as a representative of the class of ravens.

This is just one of the more obvious ways in which it can be seen how crucial a role background knowledge plays in the process of confirmation. It is not merely that it determines the effect b is to have upon the generalization g but it also decided the content of b. In other words, every i can be seen as the representative of many different classes and it is only our background knowledge which determines both how we should look at i and which of those classes we should treat it as representing.

(5) *The Search for Causal Mechanism*

In the light of the points established in the previous sections, we can take a fresh look at Hempel's paradoxes of confirmation. It is important to realize at the outset that there is no uniform solution to these paradoxes. In every situation where we find it satisfactory that the report 'Pi & Qi' should confirm the generalization $(x) (Px \supset Qx)$ but intuitively recoil from the idea that '$\sim Pi$ & $\sim Qi$' should do the same, the clue as to why this is so is to be found by examining the particular presuppositions relevant to the generalization.

Yet there is one point which appears relevant in practically all cases and we should briefly discuss it before examining particular generalizations. A generalization may be believed to be true because of the observations of individuals which positively instantiate it; the explanation *why* it is true is always believed to reside in some causal mechanism which is associated with P and ensures the occurrence of Q or is associated with $\sim Q$ which renders $\sim P$ inevitable or else there is a common cause which by a certain mechanism produces jointly P and Q or $\sim Q$ and $\sim$P. In many cases, the generalization is accepted to be well confirmed before the nature of the mechanism is discovered, yet in all cases there is a desire to discover it since we always wish to go beyong the mere knowledge that something is true and ascertain why it is true.

Now suppose that, on the basis of our background information, we expect P to contain the causal mechanism producing Q, then the reason why $(x) (\sim Qx \supset \sim Px)$ is thought to be true is the *absence* in the individual possessing $\sim Q$ of the necessary mechanism to produce Q. In all such cases, while $(x) (Px \supset Qx)$ and $(x) (\sim Qx \supset \sim Px)$ are logically equivalent, for the purposes of the actual discovery of the causal mechanism operative individuals possessing both P and Q and those lacking both P and Q are not the same. In order to discover the nature of the mechanism we are after, from a practical point of view, the examination of individuals possessing P and Q will be found much more fruitful than the examination of individuals lacking both.

Consider for a moment the generalization 'All people with malaria have been bitten by mosquitoes'. The ultimate reason for the truth of this generalization is now known to be the fact that the malaria parasite cannot attack its victims unless injected into his blood and that the parasite-carrying mosquito plays the role of injecting into the bloodstream the disease-producing agents. Even before this discovery, it was assumed, of what was known about many other diseases, that the positive factor for the conjunction of P and Q as well as of $\sim P \&$ $\sim Q$ resided in the diseased persons and that healthy people are healthy because of the absence of this factor. Now, of course, 'All who have not been bitten by any mosquito do not have malaria' is logically equivalent to the previous generalization and hence, purely from the point of view of Nicodian instantiation, a man not bitten by a mosquito and free of malaria and another man suffering from malaria who has also been bitten by a mosquito are symmetrically related to both generalizations. From the point of view of actually discovering the correct explanation for the truth of both generalizations, it is obvious that we should prefer the former individual to the latter. From a practical point of view, it is quite absurd to expect that through an examination of a healthy man we shall identify by its absence the crucial factor which failed to produce malaria. It might, therefore, be argued that, since we do not merely wish to confirm a generalization through instantiation, but also desire to place it on a much firmer footing by producing an explanation which requires its truth, we concentrate from the very beginning on individuals whose examination will help us to achieve this purpose. Other individuals which cannot be of such help to us are disregarded. This, however, does not give us the whole story of confirmation.

(6) *Natural Kinds*[1]

Perhaps the most typical case of scientific generalization is the one where, before observing any i which possesses both properties P and Q or has property P but not Q, we assume that either $(x)(Px \supset Qx)$ or that $(x)(Px \supset \sim Qx)$. The reason is that, for an individual possessing P to be interesting enough for us to wish to make generalizations about it, it is usually the case that we are already well acquainted with P and have found that all individuals possessing P have a number of other properties in common. They also uniformly lack some other properties. We also think that we know Q sufficiently to expect that it is of the type which is either uniformly possessed by or uniformly absent from all individuals having P. In such cases, the observation of a single individual possessing P will suffice to determine which one of the two generalizations we should subscribe to since we do not entertain the possibility that some individuals which possess P also posses Q while others do not.

Consider the generalization 'All lead melts at 327 °C.' As we know, virtually after the very first experiment had shown a sample of lead to melt at 327 °C., it was taken as confirmed that all lead melts at that temperature. If further experiments to determine the melting-point of other samples of lead were performed, the purpose of these was not to increase the credibility of the generalization that all lead melts at the same temperature by multiplying the observed instances of it. The sole aim of these additional experiments was to approximate more closely to the precise value of lead's melting-point by refining experimental techniques and eliminating possible sources of error. Scientists never stopped to ask themselves if perhaps the particular sample of lead experimented upon might melt at 327 °C. but others not do so. They started out with the assumption that whatever temperature represented the melting-point of one particular sample (which incidentally too is determined through a single experiment on the assumption

[1] The first version of these ideas I advanced in an essay entitled 'Natural Kinds' in the *Boston Studies in the Philosophy of Science,* iii (1968). Ideas to some extent related to these were advanced by W. V. Quine in his 'Natural Kinds', *Ontological Relativity and Other Essays* (Columbia U.P., 1969). But to my knowledge the first philosopher to suggest in general that the solution to the paradoxes lies in examining the background theories in the context of which the confirmation is made was J. L. Mackie in his 'The Paradoxes of Confirmation', *Brit. J. for the Phil. of Science,* XV (1963).

that something that melts at a given temperature on one occasion will do the same on all other occasions) was also the melting-point of all lead. The source of this attitude is to be found in the fact that all samples of lead are assumed to belong to the same natural kind with respect to melting-point.

And it is not only with respect to melting-point that lead is regarded as forming a natural kind but also with respect to coefficient of thermal expansion, specific heat, thermal conductivity, latent heat, electrical resistance, elasticity, and many other properties. Our assumptions in this case are based on what we regard as well-confirmed facts regarding other species of metals. Members of other species of metals have been found to share uniformly properties like those just mentioned. There are, of course, also many properties with respect to which all samples of lead are not regarded as constituting a natural kind, that is, properties with respect to which they are not expected all to be alike. Among these are shape, size, temperature, and velocity. This again is based on what we presume to know about other material objects.

Now consider the Hempelian logical equivalent of our generalization 'All that melts at temperatures other than 327 °C. is not lead'. It goes without saying that this generalization too will be confirmed by a single observation of lead melting at 327 °C. and to exactly the same extent as our original statement. But what about a sample of ice which is observed to melt at 0 °C. (and which is non-lead and a substance melting at a temperature other than 327 °C.), the observation of which constitutes an instance satisfying the antecedent and the consequent of the logical equivalent of our generalization?

Suppose someone were asked to determine the melting-point of lead and went ahead to observe that a sample of ice melted at 0° C. Consequently, he argued that having observed something that was not lead melting not at 327 °C. he had confirmed that lead melts at 327 °C. I am sure that we should find his reasoning not merely paradoxical or counter-intuitive but downright absurd and unacceptable. I am also quite certain that no philosopher of science would recommend that we should overcome our prejudices based on untutored common sense and accept the argument. The reason is that, without question, the argument is wrong. After all, the experiment with the sample of ice supports just as much the contention that lead melts at 100 °C. or at any other temperature than 0 °C., since 0 °C. is equally not 100° nor anything else but 0 °C.! Thus, the crucial point to recognize is that, while 'All lead melts at 327 °C.' and 'All that does not melt at 327 °C. is not lead' are logically equivalent, it is not the case that a sample of lead melting at 327 °C. and a sample of ice melting at 0 °C. are symmetrically related to either of them.

This brings us back to the important point mentioned in section (3), that every individual is concurrently a member of uncountably many classes. Ice melting at 0 °C. is a member of the class of things not melting at 327 °C., not melting at 100 °C., and so on. Before placing it in one of these classes rather than any other for the purposes of supporting some generalization concerning this class, we need some reason for doing so. There is nothing in our background knowledge nor is there anything in the outcome of our experiment which provides us with such reason.

Admittedly, the sample of lead melting at 327 °C. can be assigned to many classes. It is a material object, it is a piece of metal, it is a sample of lead of a certain shape and size, and it also belongs to the class of non-ravens, non-shoes, and so on. When we observe it melting, we could claim to have observed it melting as a representative of any of the aforementioned classes. Our background knowledge, however, provides us with good enough reasons to look upon it for the purposes of the generalization in question as a member of the class of lead. The class of non-raven or non-shoe is not regarded as forming a natural kind in any significant sense. Metals, though with respect to some properties treated as constituting a natural kind, are not so regarded with respect to melting-point. Different samples of metals are known to melt at different temperatures. On the other hand, it is compatible with the general principle to assume maximum uniformity in the behaviour of different individuals and with our previous experiences not to view our sample as a mere representative of the narrower class of lead of a certain shape and size. Thus, the resulting generalization, which we think is supported upon observing the melting of our lump of material, concerns a class of individuals we had particular reason to pick out of all the classes our sample belongs to.

A similar line of reasoning will show why there is no room to raise the paradoxes of confirmation in the case of the generalization 'All light rays travel at velocity c'. Light rays were assumed to form a natural kind with respect to speed not because this has been the case with other rays, but because it is so required by other theoretical considerations. That all light rays travel at the same velocity was assumed to be true prior to experiments which were performed solely to determine the precise value of this common velocity. Anything not travelling at c and not being a light can serve no such purpose. The same goes for Hempel's own example 'All sodium salts burn yellow'.

In the case of the generalization 'All ravens are black' the situation is somewhat different. Ravens form a natural kind with respect to quite a large number of properties, but it is clear on the basis of what we know about other species of birds that the various species fall into one of two subclasses: in one of these subclasses, all members within a species are believed to be of the same colour; in the other, members are found to differ in colour. To which subclass does the species of ravens belong? After observing a large number of ravens, all of which without exception have been black, we argue that in the case of species of birds whose members differed in colour we did not have this experience of never observing, over an extended period, anything but birds which were identical in colour. On the basis of this finding we regard it as confirmed that ravens are unlike other species of birds whose members vary.

It is evident therefore that the main significance of Hempel's paradoxes lies in the fact that they made us realize a crucial aspect of confirmation: a generalization of the form 'All P's are Q's' receives no support from the mere observation of its instances. The question of the confirmation of a hypothesis of universal conditional form is not confined to the question whether instantiations of the hypothesis have been observed. A crucial role is also played by our assumptions concerning the question whether individuals possessing P form a natural kind with respect to property Q and those possessing $\sim Q$ with respect to $\sim P$. These assumptions are shaped by our background knowledge which we acquired prior to our observing the instances of our generalization. Later we shall see that other extraneous elements too play a role in determining whether a given observation confirms a given hypothesis.

It is natural at this stage to ask what happens in totally bare contexts, when we are completely unfamiliar with the properties P and $\sim Q$ and have therefore no prior assumptions about individuals possessing these properties? It seems that if scientists were interested at all in the investigation of such individuals, they would treat those possessing P on an equal footing with those possessing $\sim Q$, and the reports 'Pi & Qi' and '$\sim Pi$ & $\sim Qi$' would be symmetrically related to the hypothesis 'All P's are Q's'. Equal confirmation would be provided by either of the two reports.

CHAPTER II

Confirmation and Parsimony

(1) *Jeffreys's Problem*

Now we shall consider generalizations of a somewhat more sophisticated nature than in the last chapter, generalizations involving the claim that an equation relating the variables representing physical parameters expresses the law governing the co-variation of these two physical parameters. An example of such a generalization is Galileo's law of free fall.

Let us begin by picturing to ourselves Galileo rolling round objects down along an inclined plane in an effort to discover experimentally the law governing the relationship between the distance travelled by the rolling body, subject to the earth's gravity, and the time taken to cover that distance. We shall imagine that at the end of seven experiments he has collected the following entirely unlikely perfect results

t	0	5	10	15	20	25	30
s	0	5	20	45	80	125	180

It seems at first that from this table of results Galileo can at once read off the law correlating time and distance

$$s = \tfrac{1}{5} t^2 \qquad\qquad (G)$$

i.e. that distance equals the square of time multiplied by a constant which, for the plane used with its particular inclination, equals $\tfrac{1}{5}$.

H. Jeffreys has, however, pointed out that there are infinitely many other equations which fit these seven results just as well as (G):

$$s = \tfrac{1}{5} t^2 + t(t-5)(t-10)\ldots(t-30)f(t) \qquad (J)$$

It should be noted that (J) is an infinite set of equations, since $f(t)$[1] may assume infinitely many different forms. Infinitely many members of the set denoted by (J) will give a different value for s

---

[1] $f(t)$ may be any expression that is a function of t.

corresponding to the next t to be tested, although for all the t's so far tested they give values of s identical with those yielded by (G). But at the same time, (J) contains an infinite subset of equations which will yield the same value of s as does (G), for the next t to be tested. It is because of this last fact that the possibility of a crucial experiment to decide between (G) and any of the (J)-equations is ruled out. For suppose we try to adjudicate between the (G)-equation and any equation belonging to (J) by testing what will happen when $t = n$. Suppose the result satisfies (G). This, of course, eliminates an infinite number of (J)-equations, but we should still be left with infinitely many equations competing with (G), namely, with all those (J)-equations, for which

$$f(t) = (t - n)\, g(t)$$

where $g(t)$ may assume infinitely many forms.

Now what exactly does our problem amount to? It would be a total misrepresentation of the situation if we said that the difficulty raised was merely that the claims of science, including even those which concern quite elementary relations like Galileo's law of free fall, are not securely founded. The situation seems rather comparable to the one in which I buy one lottery ticket where there are many billions of tickets and only one of them will be drawn to win a prize. Given that each number has an equal chance of winning, it would be wrong to say that it is merely uncertain that I shall win; the correct thing to say is that it is virtually certain that I am not going to win. Similarly, given Galileo's experimental results and the principle that the true hypothesis must satisfy them all, together with the fact that there are infinitely many hypotheses capable of doing this, we should say not merely that we cannot have full confidence that (G) stands for the law governing the correlation of distance and time but rather that it is virtually certain that (G) does not truly represent this law.

It will, of course, be noted that of all the admissible equations (G) is the simplest and therefore the most convenient of the available equations. This, however, in the absence of further argument, carries about just as much weight in favour of adopting (G) as would, in the case of the aforementioned lottery, the argument that the most convenient thing for me would be for the ticket in my possession to win, and therefore my confidence that it will win is, to some extent, justified.

One must refrain from using a number of faulty arguments which seem to present themselves and which one may be strongly tempted to employ in defending Galileo's choice of (G). Among these the most often heard is: but equation (G) works! We are much more interested in the practical aspect of science than in its capacity to produce ultimate truth. (G) has proved itself to work in the past, therefore we believe it will work in the future as well. For practical scientists that is what really matters.

This argument can be seen as faulty without our questioning the underlying assumption that whatever has worked in the past is going to work in the future as well. At this stage we shall ignore Hume's problem as to how we know that the unobserved will be like the observed or the future will be like the past. We shall assume we know. The trouble with the argument is that it overlooks the fact that there are infinitely many other equations which have also worked in the past. The argument cannot be applied to all these since infinitely many of them yield incompatible predictions. What then is there in (G) which justifies our belief that to it, rather than to its rivals, we should apply the argument that an equation which has worked in the past will work in the future as well?

Some may wish to argue that the credibility of (G) is ultimately based, not on the experimental results listed or on any further evidence of this kind, but rather on its derivability from higher-order laws and its having become an integral part of a large interconnected system known as Newtonian mechanics.

This line of approach is wrong on a number of accounts. Nobody will deny that with (G) becoming integrated into Newtonian mechanics the evidence for its truth has undergone an important qualitative change. But to claim that, until this took place, the empirical support for (G) was non-existent, would be a misrepresentation of how scientists view the situation. Galileo is not criticized for having had confidence in (G); in fact, he is admired for his efforts to establish his law of free fall by the only method available at the time, which was to test s against the various values of t. Furthermore, if we disqualified this method we should never reach a situation in which we had any higher-order laws from which to derive (G). Higher-order laws with their unifying power are only discovered on the basis of our knowledge of at least some of the laws they imply.

There is, of course, a more immediate reason as well why this line of approach is useless: Jeffrey's difficulty, which he happened to illustrate by using Galileo's laws, applies with equal force to any hypothesis, including Newton's laws, and until his problem is solved we cannot be said to have any evidence for any type of law.

Another suggestion which might seem to have merit is that, in view of all the competing equations, we should leave no t untested and thus render the problem, for practical purposes, irrelevant. From a practical point of view, the range of t is limited. If t exceeds a few minutes we are no longer in the neighbourhood of the earth's surface and (G) is not applicable. Within the limited range of zero and a few minutes, t assumes a finite number of different values since, for practical purposes, we are not interested in time intervals less than, say, one-tenth of a second. After we have determined the values of s for all the relevant values of t, the continued existence of infinitely many (J)-equations no longer needs to trouble us. All the (J)-equations left in the field yield identical results for all the tested values of t and the fact that they give different results for all the untested values of t is of no consequence since in practice we are never going to encounter those.

What is wrong with this suggestion is not merely that it may not work everywhere, since in general the range of values which are of interest to us is not as limited as in this particular case, but that it goes counter to one of the most central ideas of science. One of the main aims of the scientific enterprise is the construction of hypotheses on the basis of which we may make predictions concerning situations never before encountered. The reason why Galileo's equation is of scientific interest lies in its economy and fruitfulness, and in the fact that it is a very simple equation which has been established on the basis of a few experiments and is nevertheless capable of yielding the values of distances corresponding to a large number of yet untested values of time. Galileo regarded his law as well confirmed long before he had tested it for all the values of t which are of practical interest, and far from being condemned as a deficiency in his scientific judgement this is taken as a sign of his true insight into the nature of scientific hypotheses.

(2) *The problem of Additional Variables*

One conspicuous difference, of which we have made no mention yet, exists between equation (G) on the one hand and all the (J)-equations which remain unrefuted after a considerable number of experiments. This difference, it has struck many people, cannot be devoid of significance although it is not immediately clear what the significance is. On the one hand, it is only after we have performed all the experiments, the results of which we have tabulated, that we could put forward any particular (J)-equation, while on the other hand the (G)-equation was advanced earlier, on the basis of fewer experimental results than we have now at our disposal.

Suppose we have on our list the outcome of twenty experiments. It seems unquestionably true that equation (G) was advanced as one likely to represent the law we are after on the strength of the first five or six results, and it is quite immaterial which five or six of the twenty values of t we have tabulated were experimented on first: the same (G)-equation would have been advanced. Not so with equation (J). The twenty factors preceding $f(t)$ in the second term of the right-hand side of the equation would not have been spelled out by us (or, at any rate, it is exceedingly unlikely that they would have been spelled out) before the particular values of t, for which the distance falled is going to be determined, were known.

What exactly are we going to make of this acknowledged difference? Would it be reasonable to argue that we select equation (G) because it is much more strongly confirmed since it was advanced right after the fifth experiment and thus was confirmed by every subsequent experiment, the outcome of which could have falsified it but did not? And that we reject any particular (J)-equation which we are setting up as a rival to equation (G) and which has been advanced only now and thus has not yet been exposed to any refutation?

I do not believe that many would find such an argument very convincing. It may well be that nobody was likely to have thought of the particular (J)-equation we are now setting up as a rival to equation (*G*) before all the twenty values of *t* to be tested were known. This, however, does not amount to saying that the (*J*)-equation in question has not in fact been tested just as severely as its rival (*G*)-equation. An equation exists independently of whether anyone thinks of it and every experimental result which does not show that it cannot represent the law of free fall lends it exactly as much support as it does to equation (*G*) whether or not at the time of the experiment anyone had his mind fixed on that particular equation.

It is of course possible to point out that there is nevertheless a difference between equation (*G*) advanced fairly early in the course of the series of experiments performed and any particular (*J*)-equation put forward merely at the very completion of the series. Both of course have survived the same number of tests. In the case of the former, however, active attempts were made by the experimenter to falsify it while in the case of the latter no conscious effort was made to expose it to experimental refutation. If we agree that confirmation consists in putting a hypothesis to severe tests, with the honest intention to see whether it can survive it, then equation (*G*) has received confirmation whereas equation (*J*) has not. It is, however, hard to see why anyone should agree to such a dogmatic and arbitrary view of what confirmation comprises.

Another way to try to exploit the difference here noted between equation (*G*) and equation (*J*) is to stipulate that no equation is likely truly to represent a law of nature if it is not discovered after *m* experiments where *m* is some agreed number. We therefore perform *m* experiments and advance the various equations which we think are suggested by the outcome of these experiments. Next we perform another experiment for an additional value of *t* selected at random. If it should turn out that equation (*G*) is the only equation compatible with all the *m* + 1 results, then, now that we know the *m* + 1 value of *t*, we are not permitted to set up the appropriate rival (*J*)-equation containing the extra factor $(t - t_{m+1})$, since this would be contrary to our stipulation.

Once again it would be easy to justify such a stipulation. But there is also a much more basic reason why no suggestion attempting to exploit the difference between equation (*G*) and equation (*J*) can succeed, namely that the former could be thought of long before all the experimental results were in, while the latter would be advanced only after all the values of t were known. There is a whole group of (J)-equations which we have so far neglected to consider, each one of the infinitely many members of which can as easily be thought of and advanced as soon as equation (G).

So far we have unquestioningly assumed that for any tested value of t the value of s obtained on one occasion will be the value obtained on all occasions. Jeffreys has taken it for granted that the same value of s corresponds at all times to a given value of t and raised doubts only concerning values of s which correspond to yet untested values of t whether they will turn out as predicted on the basis of equation (G). One may, however, quite legitimately raise doubts as to whether future values of s corresponding to already tested values of t will turn out in accordance with equation (G). And what is important, one may do so without questioning the assumption that the future resembles the past or that the unobserved will be like the observed. The experimental results we have collected so far are perfectly compatible with the suggestion that the law of free fall is of the form:

$$s = \tfrac{1}{5} t^2 + A \sin \frac{N!\pi}{n} \tag{K}$$

Where N stands for some physical parameter which assumes integral values only and A and n are constant (the latter an integral). Then it is clear that as long as $N > n$, $\frac{N!\pi}{n}$ is an integer and $A \sin \frac{N!\pi}{n}$ equals zero. Thus the values so far obtained for s, instead of showing that there is no other physical parameter operative, should be taken as indicative of the fact that the third parameter had, so far, values exceeding n. N, for instance, may stand for the temperature at the centre of the earth measured on a (quantum) scale admitting of integral values only. The temperature at the centre of the earth is known constantly to be decreasing; let n be the value of the temperature to be reached in two weeks time at the centre of the earth. Clearly equation (K) is not in the least more hard to think of than equation (G), and every test for the last three centuries and for the next two weeks which support equation (G) supports equation (K) to the same degree. Both have yielded so far and will yield for another two weeks that for $s = 5$, $t = 5$, but with respect to times beyond two weeks from now $t = 5$ will correspond to some other value of s according to equation (K).[1]

It could of course be pointed out that equation (K) introduces a third variable into the picture and hence suggested that, as a matter of principle, we do not assume that an extra variable is operative until forced to do so. This suggestion would not be of much use until we justified the alleged principle. It would certainly be wrong to claim that there was anything in the evidence pointing to the absence of a third variable. All that one may say about the evidence is that it is not indicative at all that there is such a variable, but then it fails precisely to the same extent to give any indication that there is no extra variable involved.

With the introduction of a third variable we may now give our additional reason for rejecting a suggestion made in the previous section for the solution of Jeffreys's problem. It was suggested that we could eliminate all the (J)-equations that may from a practical point of view be regarded as rivals of equation (G) by performing enough experiments for every relevant value of t, which are after all limited in number. Now, of course, the suggestion is at once seen as useless since we have raised doubts about the future values of s for already tested values of t.

This latter way of rendering our problem has the advantage of clearly bringing out the fact that the difficulty with empirical inter-ference is all—pervasive, affecting the most familiar propositions of

---

[1] The problem raised here effects not only generalizations of a more soph-isticated nature where, as in Galileo's law of free fall, an equation relating vari-ables representing physical parameters expresses the law governing the co-variation of these two physical parameters. Simpler generalizations like 'All ravens are black' are equally affected. The fact that hitherto all observed ravens have been black can be expressed by

$$\frac{\text{No. of black ravens observed}}{\text{No. of ravens observed}} = 1$$

and also

$$\frac{\text{No. of black ravens observed}}{\text{No. of ravens observed}} = 1 - A \sin \frac{N!\pi}{n}$$

the two yielding different predictions.

common sense no less than the sophisticated results of advanced
science. It is easily seen that the assumption that past regularities
will continue in the future or that the unobserved resembles the
observed does not, in the least, imply even that because the sun has
risen every day in the past it is going to rise tomorrow or that
because unsupported bodies near the surface of the earth have
always fallen to the ground they will continue to do so in the future.
In prerelativistic physics, it was asserted that

$$\text{mass} = \text{constant} \qquad\qquad (L)$$

but now our attention has been drawn to the fact that all observations throughout history were compatible with the rival hypothesis
that

$$\text{mass} = \text{constant} - A \, \sin \frac{N!\pi}{n} \qquad\qquad (M)$$

where N stands for a physical parameter, the value of which drops
below n tonight for the first time in history. We have no arguments
to support the claim that (L), rather than (M), describes truly the
nature of mass. If, however, (M) is the true hypothesis, then over-
night masses will assume large negative values, setting up repulsive
forces between the earth and the sun, in consequence of which the
two will be pushed in opposite directions at such a tremendous rate
of acceleration that by the time our part of the earth turns toward
the sun, the latter will be too far away from here to appear anything
more than a very bright star. Thus the 'sun' will not rise tomorrow.
Also through the earth's gravitational force turning negative, unsupported bodies will cease to fall to the ground.

(3) *The Position of a Complete Sceptic*

I believe that, in order to make any progress toward a solution, it is
essential to realize that the notion of doubt with respect to scientific
method is very different from the notion of doubt as it applies to
some particular claim about nature once we have accepted the validity of a particular method of empirical inference.

Normally, when we entertain serious doubts about the validity of
an equation purporting to represent a law of nature, the reasonable
thing to do is suspend judgement until more evidence is forthcoming

and, in the meantime, to refrain from employing or relying on the equation in question. Suppose the questionable equation has been used in the construction of a new type of aircraft; a rational person will avoid travelling on it because of its unproved safety. Sensible people refrain from taking serious risks and, whenever the safety of a given line of action depends on the validity of a putative law of nature, they will not commit themselves to that line of action until the law in question is confirmed beyond reasonable doubt.

Suppose no one finds any solution to the difficulties we have been discussing. How is this to affect the practical conduct of our daily lives? Given, for example, that in the construction of aeroplanes the validity of all sorts of laws has been assumed without there being any way of justifying why they rather than any one of their many rivals, have been assumed to be true, is it advisable to avoid flying? The answer is that there cannot be any point in avoiding air travel when one is just as much exposed to dangers when staying on the ground. We are, after all, unable to justify our belief that the ground beneath our feet will not melt, evaporate, or explode; ought we not therefore to get off it and seek the relative safety of the air? It should be clear that since the problem we have been discussing is an all-pervasive one, affecting to the same degree every empirical proposition, there is no escape from it. Avoiding boarding aeroplanes, or not venturing outside our homes, or even lying immobile in bed will not shield us from the dangers of our environment; as long as we cannot opt out of this world we remain exposed to these dangers. Complete agnosticism with respect to scientific method is an impossibility, for being agnostic with respect to any given hypothesis implies our refusal to commit ourselves to it. Whatever we do or refrain from doing, we commit ourselves to a large number of empirical hypotheses.

The last point has the important consequence that we cannot be called reckless or be said to be taking risks when adopting any particular method of hypothesis selection, since there is no alternative we may regard as safer. The labelling of a given action as hazardous carries with it a disapprobation and implicit opinion that a different, less risky action should have been substituted in its place. Similarly, our expression of doubt implies the advocacy of the withholding of judgement and when the efficacy of a given line of action is doubted it is implied that an alternative, more secure line should be taken instead—which again cannot be held with respect to a line of action taken on the basis of any principle of hypothesis selection. Indeed, concepts such as hazard and uncertainty as well as safety, reliability, and credibility are not defined until a given scientific method is chosen, and then in relation to it. To rely on a given hypothesis may be said to be hazardous if and only if it is done not in accordance with the requirements of a scientific method to which we subscribe. When, for instance, it is said of an aircraft that it is highly reliable, and that it is extremely improbable that it should fail to land safely after take-off, it is presupposed that the laws of nature which have been relied upon in the construction of the vehicle have been confirmed in accordance with the selection principles laid down by the method universally prevailing in the scientific community and have gone through all the tests to the degree of rigour required by it. On this understanding of the notion of safety, reliability, and probability, one just cannot speak of the safety or reliability of the selection principles themselves or of the probability that they will lead to success.

What I have said so far is in broad agreement with the well-known views of Strawson. Strawson claims that to ask whether the very application of inductive standards is justified or well grounded is simply senseless; it is like asking about the legality of the law of a given country. One can inquire of a particular action of of an administrative regulation whether it is legal, which amounts to inquiring whether it is in accordance with the law; similarly one can inquire of a particular belief whether its adoption is justified, and in asking this we are asking whether the belief has been adopted in accordance with the tenets of inductive reasoning. But one cannot ask whether the law itself is legal or whether the tenets of inductive reasoning are justified. He says: 'So to ask whether it is reasonable to place reliance on inductive procedure is like asking whether it is reasonable to proportion the degree of one's conviction to the strength of the evidence. Doing this is what "being reasonable" *means* in such contexts.'[1]

[1] P. F. Strawson, *Introduction to Logical Theory* (London, 1952), p. 257.

A considerable number of philosophers have adopted Strawson's approach. Here I shall quote one of them who speaks with particular clarity:

. . . it is conceivable that induction might be less successful than some other way of reasoning about the world; this is conceivable and it is a logical possibility. But it is not probable. We know for an absolute certainty that it is not probable that any anti-inductive practice will be as successful in the long run as induction will be. Here of course I am using the term 'probable' in the sense of rational credibility, not in the relative frequency sense. Built into this normal sense of the word 'probable' is a commitment to the practice of induction. To be sure we do not know with certainty that people who practice induction will be more successful in reaching true conclusions than will those who practice some form of anti-induction; but what we do know with certainty is that those who practice induction will be probably more successful—that is, that it is reasonable to believe that they will be more successful. That this is so reflects an aspect of what the word 'probable' means in its normal sense.[1]

I shall, however, not leave matters at that. In my opinion it by no means follows from the foregoing that there is no need or possibility to defend scientific method. Admittedly, now we claim that not only can one not show that the prevailing scientific method is more assured of success than others, but that the whole notion of likelihood to succeed is inapplicable to scientific method as such. There are, however, other desiderata scientific method has to fulfil. One reasonable demand is that our method should be such that it makes maximum use of past experience in recommending the hypothesis to be selected. In what follows I shall give an outline of a defence, according to which the prevailing method is not the best method but the *only* method which is universally applicable in selecting hypotheses on the basis of past experience.

(4) *The Only Usable Methodological Principle*

It will be recognized at once, that a methodological rule requiring that, in any given situation, we choose the least simple of the admissible hypotheses would render us completely paralysed. Given any hypothesis, it is easy to construct one which is more complex than it

[1] Stephen Baker, 'Symposium on Inductive Evidence', *American Philosophical Quarterly,* ii (1965). p. 272.

and therefore, unlike the most simple, the most complex hypothesis is an undetermined and undeterminable proposition. Thus, if the problem facing us were confined to the question, should we adopt as our universal rule the principle of simplicity or the principle of maximum complexity, we should not reject the latter merely by saying that it is an inferior principle to the principle of simplicity. We would reject it because it is not a principle at all; the rule requiring us to accept the most complex of all the available hypotheses does not really require us to accept anything and is therefore not a rule in the minimal sense of that term.

The next step in my argument is to show that if we were to adopt a rule always to choose the *second* simplest of all the admissible hypotheses, or for that matter the *third, fourth,* or anything but the simplest hypothesis, we should not be provided with any means by which to decide what hypothesis to choose and should, therefore, be left without a rule.

I shall illustrate this claim with an example, which has a rather restricted applicability but which has the advantage of reflecting three important aspects of methodology.

Suppose three non-linear points are given, lying on the path of a planet known to move along a closed orbit. The simplest of all available hypotheses under these circumstances, on the assumption that the orbit consists of a continuous curve, would appear to be that the planet moves along a circular path. It will be agreed by most, that, in the absence of anything but geometrical considerations, the hypothesis with simplicity of rank two is that the orbit of the planet is elliptical.

There are, however, infinitely many ellipses which pass through the three points. Thus if we were to adopt the rule that, in any situation, one is to choose the hypothesis of rank-two simplicity we should not be provided with a definite instruction as to what specific orbit to postulate. On the other hand, the rule to choose the hypothesis of first-rank simplicity gives us the unique circle determined by the three points.

It is of great interest to note a second feature of the principle of maximizing simplicity, which is that the situation remains unchanged with respect to the basic differences between this principle and the alternative methodological principles we are comparing it with, if we wait until more points along the path of the planet are given. Suppose at some later time five points lying on the path of the planet become known, and that no circle but an ellipse passes through these points. Under these new circumstances, the hypothesis which postulated an elliptical orbit moves up to rank-one simplicity. But, under these circumstances, it is also true fortunately that no more than one ellipse passes through the points given, since through five points either no ellipse or, at most, one ellipse may be drawn.

This then is a small illustration of what I suggest may be universally the case: while other principles of selection lead us to a whole set of hypotheses of a certain kind, the principle of picking the simplest of all hypotheses generally leads us to pick a unique hypothesis. And although what is the simplest hypothesis changes with changing circumstances, it is an invariable aspect of our principle that is usable.

Before leaving this example, let me raise a crucial third point which may be made with its aid. On the surface, it may seem that the following question could be posed: even though our data consist of no more than three non-linear points on the path of the planet under investigation, any ellipse we may draw through these points is just a concrete, specific, and uniquely different from any other curve as is the circle determined by the three points. What then is the basis for saying that this unique curve, which is perfectly compatible with our data, is less likely to represent the orbit of our planet than the circle?

The answer to this question lies in the realization of the essential idea that we are not considering the prior probability of any putative hypothesis. We are approaching the matter from the point of view of the *rules* according to which a hypothesis is adopted. Any curve which passes through our three points is unique, but it is only in the case of the circle that we can name the universal methodological principle which has directed us specifically to postulate it, rather than any other curve, as the shape of the orbit of our planet.

Ultimately, then, our adherence to the principle of maximizing simplicity is seen to be caused by the indeterminate nature of all alternative rules. All ellipses which pass through the three points are symmetrical with respect to one another. Why pick this ellipse rather than that? The principle of choosing the hypothesis of rank-two simplicity seems to operate symmetrically with respect to all the infinitely many ellipses. No other principle which singles out this ellipse and is also universally applicable and which could provide grounds for our choice seems to present itself. We can, however, explain why we pick the circle we do pick; sufficient reason for our choice can be provided: it is uniquely given by the rule which instructs us to choose the hypothesis that is compatible with the data and is the simplest of those which satisfy them.

Now we may return to our previous examples. Until the beginning of the twentieth century, our experience allowed us to describe mass by

$$\text{mass} = \text{constant} \qquad\qquad (L)$$

or by

$$\text{mass} = \text{constant} + F(x) \qquad\qquad (N)$$

where $F(x)$ reduces to zero for all past observations. The principle of maximizing parsimony bids us select (L). I should point out that we are not ignoring the fact that there are difficulties in exhaustively characterizing the notion of simplicity. However, no matter how intricate these difficulties may be in general, in the present context the selection of the most parsimonious of all the available equations is a straightforward matter. It is our good fortune that, in all the situations associated with the general problem we are considering (namely, where for every hypothesis advanced that is compatible with the data infinitely many others are automatically generated) it is immediately obvious which is the most parsimonious of all these: that equation, the terms on the right-hand side of which form a proper subset of all the terms on the right-hand sides of the other equations, is the most parsimonious of all.

Which of the equations is of rank-two parsimony? Let $F^*(x)$ be the simplest $F(x)$, then it is clear that

$$\text{mass} = \text{constant} + F^*(x) \qquad\qquad (N^*)$$

is the equation of rank-two parsimony. Suppose we adopted the rule of choosing the rank-two hypothesis, then, of course, we should have to face the difficulty of how to identify $F^*(x)$ since we have no generally applicable criterion for the ordering of mathematical expressions with respect to their simplicity. This, however, may not be an insurmountable difficulty as there is no reason to believe that such a criterion may, in principle, never be constructed. The real difficulty is that x may stand for indefinitely many physical parameters and thus (N^*) represents not a single equation but an equation form. Here again then, in this much more general situation, we find exactly what we found in our more specific example, that if we adopt the principle of maximizing parsimony, we are led to the choice of a specific hypothesis, namely, that (L) describes properly the nature of mass. If we were to adopt, however, a rule of choosing the hypothesis of rank-two parsimony, we should be presented with an indefinitely large set to choose from without being provided with sufficient reason as to why we should prefer a specific equation of type (N^*) over another.

The second point made earlier, concerning what happens when with an increase in our knowledge one hypothesis comes to be replaced by another as being the most parsimonious in the context of the new situation, is well illustrated here too. With the acquisition of knowledge that led to the adoption of Special Relativity, the most parsimonious expression describing the behaviour of mass became

$$\text{mass} = \text{constant} + F(v) \qquad (R)$$

where v is the velocity of the body whose mass is measured relative to the system in which it is measured.

Once again, there are infinitely many equations which are equivalent to (R) with respect to all past observations, namely

$$\text{mass} = \text{constant} + F(v) + G(x) \qquad (S)$$

where $G(x)$ reduces to zero for all those observations. Suppose $G^*(x)$ is the simplest form of $G(x)$, then

$$\text{mass} = \text{constant} + F(v) + G^*(x) \qquad (S^*)$$

is the equation of rank-two simplicity describing mass in a manner compatible with contemporary knowledge. But again, while (R) is a single equation, (S^*) represents an indefinite number of equations, since x may stand for all sorts of physical parameters. Thus the principle of parsimony yields a unique hypothesis, while the principle of selecting a hypothesis with any degree of parsimony other than the first fails to yield a unique hypothesis. This, of course, is not too surprising. The crucial advantage of the principle of parsimony over all other principles described here is a necessary consequence of the very notion of parsimony. The most parsimonious of all the equations which will fit all that has been observed is the one which is free of all extraneous[1] elements. There is only one way of being free of all extraneous elements; there are infinitely many ways of having such an element: by having *any* one term which is extraneous.[2]

[1] It should be clear that the extraneous element is not necessarily, as in the case before us, a term; it may also be a factor or an index. For example the equation

$$\text{mass} = \text{constant} \times \cos \frac{T!\pi}{n}$$

is, as long as $T > n$, equivalent to

$$\text{mass} = \text{constant}$$

and is a less parsimonious rival to the latter, containing the extraneous element $\cos \frac{T!\pi}{n}$.

It is important to realize that each one of the infinitely many less parsimonious rival hypotheses h' of the most parsimonious hypothesis h is parasitic upon the latter. h' is formed from h by adding to it an extra element such that both h and h' are equally confirmed by any member of a set of evidence e' any member of which, if it confirms h, does not confirm h', and if it confirms h', does not confirm h. h may, of course, sometimes have genuine rivals which are not parasitic upon it, in the way Copernican celestial mechanics rivalled Ptolemy's or Young's theory of light rivalled Newton's. Such hypotheses require, however, the services of a creative scientist; they are not mass produced. Such rival hypotheses do not present an important philosophical problem: since there are never more than a few of them they are eliminated by crucial evidence which supports one hypothesis and not the other. Of course, there is always specific evidence which will adjudicate between any h' and h and hence, if h is the correct hypothesis, h' will drop out of the competition because of that evidence. But as there are infinitely many h's, no matter how many are eliminated through the use of crucial evidence, there are still infinitely many left to compete with h.

[2] If there were an aspect other than parsimony which different hypotheses possessed to different degrees and it were clear in every case which hypotheses possessed it to a maximum degree, then it may very well be that a principle to maximize that aspect would also enable us to choose a unique hypothesis in all cases.

For a moment it might seem perhaps that we could adopt some other principles as well which would always yield a unique hypothesis. It might be suggested in a fanciful way, for instance, that, in order to overcome the problem of not being provided with a specific hypothesis whenever we required one, we should appoint a certain person as our Hypothesis Chooser whose task it would be to give clear instructions in every instance what hypothesis we should subscribe to. Alternatively, it might be suggested that, whenever presented with a set of hypothesis all compatible with past observations, we should choose the one we think of first.

Now it is unquestionably true that there are innumerable rules one could adopt to pick out always a particular hypothesis compatible with past observations and which would yield concrete predictions. We could agree, for example, on the rule that of all the competing hypotheses we should choose the one to be adopted by drawing lots or that the United Nations should appoint a Universal Hypothesis Chooser, whose task it would be to pick one hypothesis, out of all those which have so far accounted for all the events of the past, for the whole world to adopt. Thus, it would not seem impossible to adopt the convention that the phrase 'the future will resemble the past' should be taken to mean that the future will resemble the past as described by the statement picked out by any one of the aforementioned rules.

Momentarily it may seem, therefore, that our original problem has shifted to the next level: we now appear to require a meta-rule to help us to decide which first-order rule to adopt for the selection of hypotheses. But it will easily be recognized that the first-order rule which has universally been adopted is different from all other possible rules. For, although it is true that, no matter which convention we adopted, the future would be assumed to resemble the past

---

I have no proof that such an aspect does not exist. But in order to raise an objection of real interest to my suggestion it would first have to be clearly explained what this aspect was, how to recognize it and distinguish its different degrees, and why it is in all cases easily determinable which of the infinitely many hypotheses compatible with the data possesses this aspect to a maximum degree. Furthermore and most importantly it would have to be explained why, while the hypothesis which possesses the aspect in question to a maximum degree is unique, hypotheses which possess it to any other given degree are infinitely many.

according to some description of the past, there would be nothing in the past events and the types of regularities exhibited by these which *in itself* determined which particular description we should choose for projecting into the future. Only according to the prevailing convention (i.e. the first order rule to maximize parsimony is it the case that the past is assumed to determine the future in a *strong sense*. The future behaviour of masses is predicted on the basis of their past behaviour without appeal to anything extraneous (e.g. the drawing of lots or a special person). It entirely depends on the nature of past events what regularities these exhibit and which statement corresponds to the most parsimonious true description of these.[1]

(5)   *A Defence of the Induction Principle*

Now we are in a position to say something about the problem of induction in general. What is the problem of induction? There are not many people who, in the twentieth century, have restated the problem of induction more lucidly than Bertrand Russell in a chapter called 'On Induction' in his book *The Problems of Philosophy*. He begins his exposition with an example:

---

[1] Suppose now it is objected: admittedly the selection principle according to which we are to adopt the most parsimonious of the available hypotheses is indeed different from all other such principles inasmuch as it alone relies on nothing extraneous to the listed results of our observations. But the selection principle according to which we are to subscribe to the hypothesis provided for us by the Universal Hypothesis Chooser appointed by the U.N. is unique too inasmuch as it alone ensures that we always adopt the hypothesis selected by the special person assigned to the task. Thus what makes us adopt the principle according to which the future is determined by the past in a strong sense, which is unique in one way, rather than another principle, such as the one just mentioned, which is unique in another way?

The answer to this question is similar to the answer to the question, why, if we do employ the principle of assuming that the future is like the past in the strong sense, should we select the most parsimonious rather than the second or third most parsimonious hypothesis: it is only through the practice we have adopted that we end up with something determinate. If we are permitted to use anything extraneous to our observations, such as a Universal Hypothesis Chooser, then infinitely many candidates present themselves and there is no way to select among the infinitely many diverse selection principles which these employ. Only if we adopt the rule not to admit any extraneous elements do we have a unique principle of hypothesis selection which also selects a unique hypothesis, namely the most parsimonious hypothesis.

Let us take as an illustration a matter about which none of us in, fact, feel the slightest doubt. We are all convinced that the sun will rise tomorrow... It is obvious that, if we are asked why we believe that the sun will rise tomorrow, we shall naturally answer, 'Because it always has risen every day.' We have a firm belief that it will rise in the future, because it has risen in the past. If we are challenged as to why we believe that it will continue to rise as heretofore, we may appeal to the laws of motion: the earth, we shall say, is a freely rotating body, and such bodies do not cease to rotate unless something interferes from outside, and there is nothing outside to interfere with the earth between now and tomorrow. Of course, it might be doubted whether we are quite certain that there is nothing outside to interfere, but this is not the interesting doubt. The interesting doubt is as to whether the laws of motion will remain in operation until tomorrow. (pp. 33—4).

He goes on to explain why this doubt cannot be resolved through any argument based on our knowledge of the past:

It has been argued that we have reason to know the future will resemble the past, because what was the future has constantly become the past, so that we really have experience of the future, namely of times which were formerly future, which we may call past futures. But such an argument really begs the very question at issue. We have experience of past futures, but not of future futures, and the question is: Will future futures resemble past futures? (pp. 35—6).

It seems to be implied that if the question 'Will future futures resemble past futures' could be answered in the affirmative, then we could rest assured about tomorrow's sunrise; our only cause for worry is our inability to provide an affirmative answer. Russell appears quite clearly to be maintaining that if it were given that there had been no outside interference to stop the rotation of the earth and yet the sun failed to rise, this would constitute an example that nature cannot be relied upon to remain always unchanged and future events do not necessarily continue to obey the past regularities. But this, as we have seen in Section (2) of this chapter, is not so. The sun may fail to rise tomorrow because masses have always obeyed and continue to obey equation (M) rather than equation (L). Clearly then the inductive principle does not merely bid us to assume that its future will be like the past, but that the future will be like the past in accordance with the most parsimonious description thereof.

In the light of what we have said on the previous section, however, the Russellian way of describing induction does not necessarily appear faulty. It need not be objectionable to express oneself in the manner of Russell as long as it may be assumed to be understood that 'the future will be like the past' is merely short for '. . . like the past described in a particular fashion everyone knowing in which particular fashion, namely, in accordance with the most parsimonious description'. The reason why it can be assumed that this is what is meant is that there does not seem to exist any other way of interpreting the principle. As we have seen in the previous section, any other interpretation either does not really allow us to make predictions on the assumption of the strict similarity of past and future alone (since one is required to employ extraneous factors beside one's knowledge of past regularities exhibited by the event type we are connected with) or does not allow us to make any specific predictions at all because it renders one's principles indeterminate.

Now we are in a position to see the outlines of a possible defence of induction in general. This defence presupposes that all agree that no guarantee whatever can be given that any method of predicting the future yields correct results. On the other hand, it is also understood that we cannot refrain from acting altogether and therefore we must subscribe to some method of hypothesis selection. In view of this it may be sufficient to show that the method adopted is superior to any of its alternatives.

Suppose we agree that it is an essential desideratum that all our hypotheses about the unobserved should be constructed on the basis of what is equally accessible to all people. We shall take it for granted that the raw material upon which our principle of empirical reasoning is to operate, is the observed facts of the kind about which we are to hypothesize.

It would seem then that the method which arrives at conjectures based on past observations through the principle of assuming the resemblance of the future and the past has an edge over all alternative 'methods'; it is the only method capable of being applied to experience.

Suppose it were recommended that we should employ the principle—which sometimes has been called 'counterinductive'—of always assuming that the future will be unlike the past. Does the principle bid us assume that the future will not be like the past as it is described by inductivists? Such an assumption leads us nowhere, as it does not yield determinate predictions; there are infinitely many ways in which the future may differ from the past. Thus, this version of counterinduction offers no methodology at all. But we should be no better off if we were to assume that the future will not be like the past as described in any other particular way.

Is it perhaps feasible to employ the principle of assuming that the unobserved will not be like the past as described in any but one particular way? Which particular way are we to take as being singled out by this principle? Surely not the most complex one, since, as we have already said, that simply does not exist. But descriptions of parsimony of rank two as well as of rank three and, in fact, of any other rank but one, exist in infinitely large numbers and we should be provided with no means of choosing a particular hypothesis among all the hypotheses of equal rank. Only the description which contains no redundant elements is a unique description of the observed in the sense that every other description differs from it in the rank of the parsimony it possesses. But, of course, if the principle of assuming that the future will not be like the past is to be interpreted to mean that it will not be like the past as it is described in any but the most parsimonious way, then the principle is equivalent to the inductive principle. The latter, therefore, appears to be the only principle which leads to the choice of a determinate hypothesis, among the infinitely many hypotheses which are automatically generated by the addition of terms extraneous with respect to the past, and provides us with a methodology of coping with the future by means of a rule applicable to past observations.[1]

---

[1] It is being assumed throughout that the mathematics we work with and the language in which we formulate our statements are the ones in common use. We do not, for example, admit artificially constructed predicates such as grue and bleen. Apart from all the obvious objections to such predicates from considerations of simplicity and teachability there is the objection that there are infinitely many possible artificially created words and there are infinitely many diverse predictions we are led to make through the use of the various artificial predicates. But there is no criterion to guide us how to choose among these predicates; thus, there is nothing to tell us which of the contrary predictions to accept. If we stick, however, to natural languages we have no problem as their use yields a unique prediction in all cases. Thus the principle of using a natural language, and it alone, produces determinate predictions.

CHAPTER III

Confirmation and Confirmability

(1) *Factors which Play a Role in Confirmation*

In this chapter I should like to elaborate upon one of the crucial features of confirmation brought out in the last chapter, a feature not always acknowledged yet whose importance, in my opinion, cannot be overemphasized: all confirmation is essentially a two-staged process. First we determine that observation b confirms hypothesis h relative to T (where T is a set of sentences including h which together entail b); next we have to inquire how T compares with other theories which too may entail b and are thus confirmed by it also. We cannot say that b confirms h in an absolute sense until we have satisfied ourselves that b confirms h relative to the most acceptable of the theories which imply b.

Now the following difference between inductive and deductive logic is fairly well known: given that a set of true observation statements logically implies h, then h is true and remains so, no matter what further observations are made. However, when h receives merely inductive support from b then subsequently this support may be rendered wholly ineffectual in the light of additional observations which do not necessarily conflict with b.

For example let 'b_1' stand for 'several samples of lead have been observed to melt at 327 °C.; then in the light of b_1 the hypothesis 'All lead melts at 327 °C.' ($=$'h') is regarded as strongly confirmed. Suppose we are in addition given 'b_2', namely 'other samples of lead have been observed melting at 500 °C.' which is logically compatible with b_1, then in the light of b_2 we shall regard h as strongly disconfirmed.

So far, however, no reason has been provided why we must renounce the claim that logical implication and inductive confirmation are similar in that they are both dyadic relationships; the former obtaining between premiss and conclusion, the latter between evidence and hypothesis. It may still seem possible to maintain that it is the empirical evidence and it alone which determines whether or not a given hypothesis is confirmed. But with the availability of b_2 it is no longer the case that our evidence consists of b_1 for it now amounts to b_c, which is the conjunction of b_1 and b_2 and is clearly differently related to h than is b_1.

However, in view of the crucial fact, discussed at great length in the previous chapter, that any set of observations can be accounted for by infinitely many sets of lawlike sentences, we must concede that confirmation is a more complex relationship. Suppose we computed the weird orbit which the earth would describe in its journey relative to the sun for the next six months if the law governing the behaviour of masses were given by a specific instance of the equation form:

$$\text{mass} = \text{constant} + F(x) \qquad\qquad (N)$$

What is the status of the hypothesis that the orbit thus arrived at rather than the one arrived at on the assumption that masses are constant, is going to be the actual orbit of the earth?

Seeing that all our past observations follow from (N) our hypothesis is strongly confirmed relative to the theory that (N) governs the behaviour of masses. The hypothesis, however, is not confirmed in an absolute sense since, among all the theories which imply the same set of observations, the theory relative to which it is confirmed is not the most acceptable one.

About the assumption itself that (N) governs the behaviour of masses we can say either that it is a candidate for confirmation, since it entails all our observations concerning the behaviour of masses, but it is not actually confirmed, since there is another candidate superior to it, or once again that it receives relative confirmation (i.e. relative to itself), but not absolute confirmation, since it is inferior to the most parsimonious assumption.

The importance of the availability of alternative theories is well dramatized in an example adopted from Reichenbach which I shall describe presently. In this example we find that we abandon a hypothesis, although not a single observation hostile to it has been made, simply because someone succeeds in constructing an alternative theory in which all our observations are accounted for without that hypothesis. It may even happen that the fact that E_1 confirms

H relative to *T* confers credibility upon *H* since *T* is acceptable, but that later, without the discovery of any new evidence, *H* loses its credibility simply because someone succeeds in constructing an alternative theory in which E_1 is accounted for without *H*. Let me illustrate this with an example adopted from Reichenbach.

We shall imagine a fictitious situation in which the state of pure geometry is 150 years behind that in which it is today, while space-travel technology is hundreds of years ahead of ours: manned inter-galactic rockets can travel anywhere with any desired speed. Suppose it is found upon exploration of space that all galaxy clusters are housed within the (comparatively thin) inner and outer walls of an entirely closed huge spherical shell.

One day after the discovery of a fuel which lasts indefinitely, an astronaut decides to do the journey between two diametrically opposed points on the shell, not, as always has been done hitherto, via the galaxy-filled space within its walls but via the centre of the sphere, crossing the unexplored ocean of void. After traversing hugh distances of empty space he reaches, to his surprise, another galaxy-filled spherical shell. He explores this new shell-universe and finds it to be similar in every respect to the only one hitherto known to have existed; he discovers in it a galaxy identical with ours with its familiar solar system containing the exact replica of our Earth. Landing on this 'earth' he encounters the perfect image of his town, street, and house, inhabited with his acquaintances, wife, and children with whom he is able to continue conversations he began before setting out on his journey and who express surprise at finding him returning from a direction opposite from that expected. Determined to get to the centre of the universe, the astronaut leaves this shell in the inward direction, only to discover more and more shell-universes identical with it.

In order to explain his experiences he cannot simply say that each time he has returned to his original shell since, for one thing, he was travelling along a straight line away from his point of origin all the time and, secondly, he reached the second shell from the outside. He is forced to assume, therefore, that the universe consists of infinitely many identical shells which run like synchronized clocks. In each of these shell-universes there lives a person exactly like himself with life history, experiences, and memory identical to his own, and just as he was leaving his home all his replicas were leaving their respective homes toward their respective inward neighbouring shell. He must also postulate that, as one moves inward toward the centre, one contracts in size. This will explain why the inner shells which cannot but be smaller in dimension than the outer ones nevertheless appear to him identical with the outer shells in shape as well as in size: it is because his measuring instruments as well as his space-ship and his body have undergone a proportional contraction. This also accounts for the fact that he can go on discovering more and more shells without ever reaching their common centre: since he is contracting in size as he is moving toward it, just at the right rate so that each new shell appears to him exactly of the size of the one he has just left, the distance between him and the centre, in terms of his measuring instruments, remains for ever unaltered.

But at a later stage it occurs to some geometricians to construct geometries based on sets of axioms which differ from the set on which Euclid based his geometry and to note that innumerably many of these are possible. They also find that in some of these there exists a space with topological properties in which the relationship 'enclosing' and 'enclosed' as applying to spherical surfaces with a common centre is not determined and you may get from one point on the 'inner' surface of a shell to a point on the 'outer' surface not only by crossing through the shell but also by passing along a straight line perpendicular to the surface and away from it toward the centre. At this stage we have an alternative way of explaining the discoveries of our space-traveller. It is no longer necessary to assume that there are infinitely many universes identical with one another, except for size, nor is it required that we should postulate that physical length varies with distance from the centre of the universe. Instead, we may assume that the topology governing our universe is the one just described and that the traveller, even though he never reversed his direction, simply returned to the same unique earth from which he set out upon his journey.

Let then the hypothesis that, as one moves perpendicular to the shell containing the galaxies, one's size undergoes a change, be denoted by *H*, and the experiences of the astronaut by *B*. Does *B* confirm *H*? The answer is that relative to the theory *T*, which consists of the assumption that space is Euclidean, and that the universe consists of infinitely many concentric shells, it does. But *B* also confirms *H* absolutely as long as there is no other theory to compete with *T*. However, without the introduction of any new empirical evidence at all, but simply by the discovery of the possibility of an alternative theory to *T*, namely that there is only one shell but space is non-Euclidean, *E* suddenly ceases to confirm *H* absolutely, since it confirms it relative only to *T*, which has a rival that is at least as good as *T*.

(2) *Relative and Absolute Confirmation*

Before we can say that given evidence lends some degree of credibility to a certain hypothesis, we must determine the theory relative to which the evidence confirms the hypothesis and examine whether the theory is acceptable. The first step is carried out by finding a set of statements *T* which include *h* and which logically imply the evidence. The second step will be discussed in the next section. Every hypothesis is confirmed relative to some theories but, in most cases, relative to unacceptable theories. Consider for example 'There is life on Venus'. It is confirmed relative to the theory which contains both it and 'If there is life on Venus then snow is white', since together they entail the observation statement 'Snow is white' not entailed by either of them on its own. But this does not lend it any credibility at all (not even empirical significance as we shall see later), for not only does this 'theory' have the empirical range of the simpler theory 'snow is white' which entails that snow is white and is hence preferable to it, but we have also the rival hypothesis 'There is no life on Venus' which together with 'If there is no life on Venus then snow is white' entails that 'snow is white'. A hypothesis may have been deemed to have received credibility through some evidence, since the theory relative to which the evidence confirmed that hypothesis was an acceptable one, and later lose its credibility, because the theory is replaced by a rival theory which is either newly discovered or rendered superior by new evidence.

All this is quite simple but by no means universally appreciated; nor is it immediately evident in all cases. Consider, for example, '*h*' which stands for 'all ravens are black' and which is taken as being confirmed by the sighting of black ravens. Here it may appear that the confirmation of *h* is solely determined by the nature of our observations and that no further factors play any role. But this is not so. Here, as elsewhere, *b* confirms *h* in an absolute sense because *b* confirms *h* relative to *T* where *T* is preferable to all its rivals which also entail *b* and in some of which the contrary of *h*, *h**, is asserted, where '*h**' stands for At most 1 per cent of all ravens are black'. For though it is true that *h* together with 'The thing I am observing is a raven' entails '*b*', i.e. 'the thing I am observing is black', it is also true that *h** plus 'All the ravens I am observing belong to that small minority group of ravens, the colour of which deviates from the normal' together with 'The thing I am observing is a raven' entail that the thing is black, while no two of the last three statements on their own entail it. Thus ultimately which one of the many theories implying that the thing I observe is black is taken to be confirmed by that observation is determined by which of these theories is superior to all others. Suppose I am visiting a zoo which specializes in rare animals and contains only those members of any given species which are unusually coloured, that is, whose colour differs from that of at least 99 per cent of the members of the species. Let us also suppose that I have no prior information about the colour of ravens and that in one of the cages I observe a number of black ravens. I do not believe it will be disputed that under such circumstances I should be entitled to treat my observation as leading credibility to the hypothesis that most ravens are not black rather than that all of them are black.

It may be objected that while the case of the astronaut's discovery proves the claim that confirmation is a triadic relationship, the last example could be accommodated under the orthodox view in which confirmation is a relation between evidence and hypothesis alone. It could be claimed that when the evidence consists of the observation of a black raven then the evidence absolutely confirms that all ravens are black. In the second case where we regard 'Not all ravens are black' as being confirmed the evidence is different from what it was before; what we have is the observation of a black raven plus the observation that we are in a special zoo.

Let us, therefore, confine our attention to the case where black ravens are observed under normal circumstances. It is still the case that an alternative theory is constructible under which the observation of a black raven is to be construed as evidence that not all ravens are black. According to this theory, as long as the temperature at the centre of the earth is above a certain temperature, normal ravens are inaccessible to human observations and only ravens with unusual colour can be seen. The temperature at the centre of the earth is constantly decreasing and, on our theory, it will soon reach the temperature which permits normal ravens to be observed, after which the overwhelming majority of ravens will be observed to have a colour different from black. Admittedly, there is no evidence, and could be no evidence, for the theory according to which the ravens hitherto observed were normal ravens representative of their species. It is only that this is the theory which, because of its greater simplicity, we prefer. Thus the observation of a black raven under the usual circumstances is taken as absolute confirmation of 'All ravens are black' not because the evidence only supports this theory but because this theory, when compared with its rivals, is deemed superior to them.

Let me conclude this section by indicating how, in the light of what has been said, certain difficulties, such as Hempel's well-known puzzle concerning his converse-consequences condition, disappear. According to the *c-c* condition, if a statement confirms a hypothesis *h*, it also confirms every hypothesis which entails that hypothesis. This condition, which is perfectly correct in our view, has been declared untenable. Were the *c-c* condition adopted says Hempel, then any evidence would confirm any hypothesis. Let *b* be any evidence and *h* any hypothesis. Observing that *b* is true confirms *b* and, by the *c-c* condition, *h.b* also since *h.b* entails *b*. But according to the rule Hempel calls 'the special consequence condition', which says that if an observational report confirms a statement it also confirms every consequence of that statement, *b* which confirms *h.b* confirms also *h* which is a consequence of *h.b*.[1]

[1] C. G. Hempel, *Aspects of Scientific Explanation* (New York, 1965), p. 32.

But we have already conceded that anything can be confirmed relative to some theory without this raising any difficulties. Undesirable results would only follow if it could be shown that anything is confirmed *absolutely* by everything. The relation of *h.b* to *b* is no more privileged than that of ~*h.b* which also entails it. In fact, both conjunctive statements are inferior to *b* which accounts for the same observation and is simpler than either of them. Our observing that *b* is true confirms in an absolute sense *b* alone and nothing else.

(3)   *The Choice among Rival Theories*

On the view propounded here, to determine whether a given statement is made credible to any degree by the available evidence, one has to perform a two-stage test. The first stage is a fairly simple one: one has to ascertain the theory relative to which a given statement may be regarded as confirmed by the evidence. The second stage, however, is a somewhat more complicated procedure: to determine the status of that theory as compared with other theories. Whether the theory relative to which that evidence confirms the hypothesis is superior to its rivals. But when is a theory T_1 superior to T_2? In the very special case in which T_1 and T_2 account for exactly the same set of observations and the postulates of T_1 form a proper subset of the postulates of T_2, we have a clear-cut situation in which T_2 has redundant elements that T_1 does away with: hence T_1 is simpler and therefore superior to T_2. In general, however, to judge the relative merits of competing theories is not so straightforward a matter.

Consider, for example, the situation with respect to the two planetary hypotheses—the Ptolemaic and the Copernican—in the sixteenth century. The number of epicycles employed by the two systems was comparable, as was the accuracy with which they accounted for the movements of the various planets. However, Ptolemy, in order to account for the limited elongation of the inferior planets, had to resort to the *ad hoc* device of aligning the centre of the epicylces of the inferior planets with the Sun and the Earth, something Copernicus could dispense with. On the other hand, Copernicus had to postulate that there were at least two centres of motion in the universe, the Sun for the planets and the Earth for the moon while for Ptolemy everything in the universe revolved around a single centre. Moreover, Copernicus had to postulate the existence of a vast space between the sphere of the furthest planet and the sphere of fixed stars, or he could not explain how it was that, in the course of the Earth's long journey around the Sun, no parallax could be observed. These are just a few examples picked from a group of phenomena relevant to the competing planetary systems, some of which were better assimilated by one system and thus militated against its rival, while others had the opposite effect. Scientists did not have any method whereby the sum of the various advantages and disadvantages could be precisely calculated. How then were they to settle the question, which planetary theory to adopt?

The answer to this question brings me to a crucial point, to be elaborated in the last chapter, around which turns the essential difference between scientific statements, on the one hand, and meta-scientific statements (like the one expressing the doctrine of determinism), on the other. Scientific statements are about natural phenomena. In a given stage of the history of science the comparative merits of two theories purporting to describe the laws governing a group of natural phenomena may be undecidable. There are, however, innumerably many phenomena which we believe logically interconnected. With time, therefore, more phenomena relevant to these theories are bound to come to our notice and, with the advance of knowledge, evidence accumulates which is more easily assimilated by one theory and hence hostile to the other which is consequently more and more difficult to maintain. In the sixth century B.C. the relative merits of the round-earth hypothesis and the flat-earth hypothesis may not have been decidable. But then someone thought of explaining lunar eclipses as being caused by the spherical earth's shadow and of explaining the way ships disappear and reappear on the horizon by the fact that the earth curves downwards at the horizon. More and more facts came to light, which under the flat-earth hypothesis were either inexplicable or had to be accounted for by elaborate hypotheses specially postulated for the purpose. This made the round earth inevitably—since we believe it to be the true hypothesis—and increasingly the more acceptable hypothesis, as it could handle ever better than its rival the accumulating evidence relevant to the shape of the earth.

A similar process was at work in the case of the competing planetary theories. With the discovery of Jupiter's moons it became evident that no account of the solar system which assigned to it a single centre of motion was possible; later with the discovery of parallax the objection arising from its apparent absence vanished; Newtonian mechanics accounted for the mechanism whereby no extra moving power was required if all planets revolved around the more massive Sun; and so on.

This then may be said to be generally the case with scientific theories; the false theory is bound to come into direct or indirect conflict with innumerably many facts. To smooth over this conflict it has to be encumbered with complicating qualifications and extra hypotheses. Its inability effectively to cope with the facts sooner or later becomes overwhelmingly clear.

The observational basis of meta-scientific theories on the other hand, as we shall see, is science. An assertion or denial that the world is strictly deterministic rests upon our findings of how science is. Unlike statements about natural phenomena which are endlessly many, there are very few meta-scientific statements. When conflicting statements of the first order account with comparable efficiency for a given range of phenomena, other phenomena will become known which will shift the ground in support of one of them; when conflicting statements of the second order or metaphysical statements account with comparable efficiency for the way science is, no such process can be counted upon to settle the issue. This then is ultimately the reason why scientific disputes are eventually settled while metaphysical controversies may continue unresolved. But more about this later.

(4) *Confirmability in Principle*
The most valuable dividend gained from a proper understanding of the process of confirmation is the disappearance of the seemingly recalcitrant problem of how precisely to define confirmability (or verifiability) in principle, and hence how to set up a criterion whereby to distinguish the empirically significant from what is devoid of such significance. The one thing which we must have firmly fixed in our minds in this connection is that a statement is verifiable in principle

if and only if circumstances are describable under which it would be confirmed.

Now it may seem that such a principle, first of all, says very little that is not known and accepted universally and, secondly, surely cannot carry us very far.

To the first objection, let me point out that, while it may appear that the principle says nothing that is not accepted by everyone anyhow as the definition of verifiability, in practice philosophers often manage to violate it. A case in point is that of Professor W. Salmon, who is one of the few writers in recent years to express a belief that the verifiability principle is viable.

He poses the following problem:[1] Let S and N stand for a meaningful and meaningless sentence, respectively. We have the following two logical relations:

(i) $S \rightarrow S \vee N$

(ii) $[(S \vee N). \sim S] \rightarrow N$

Now, if we accept, as we are bound to accept, the principle that whatever is entailed by a verifiable statement (and is not necessarily true) is itself verifiable, then by (i) and (ii) combined, N is verifiable. Furthermore, if we identify factual meaningfulness with empirical verifiability, then we are involved in a contradiction as well, since a sentence we have stipulated to be nonsensical has just been shown to be meaningful.

In order to solve the difficulty, Salmon advances a number of principles concerning truth-functional expressions containing meaningless components. One of these principles is that, given S and N, a meaningful and meaningless sentence respectively, $S \vee N$ is identical in meaning to S. This, Salmon claims, destroys the validity of (ii) and thus N cannot be derived from verifiable premises.

Without questioning his rules or his claim that they are effective in destroying (ii), surely Salmon should have asked himself whether he had not achieved rather too much too soon. For example, way back in the 1930s Ayer made the famous suggestion that a statement be regarded as verifiable and consequently meaningful

[1] *Mind, Matter and Method,* edited by P. Feyerabend and G. Maxwell (Minneapolis, 1966), pp. 363–8.

if some observation statement can be deduced from it in conjunction with certain other premises, without being deducible from those other premises alone. Against this Isaiah Berlin pointed out[1] that a criterion of meaning which allows such latitude as this is unacceptable, since any piece of nonsense N, provided only that it had the grammatical form of an indicative sentence, could be shown verifiable since N in conjunction with $N \supset O$ implies O where O is and observation sentence. As a result of this criticism, Ayer revised his criterion. Was it really necessary? Could he not simply, by adopting Salmon's approach, argue that, since $N \supset O$ is identical in meaning with O, the auxiliary premiss itself implies O in violation of his criterion?

But it seems clear that Salmon has failed to realize that his rules, however valuable they may be, can only be applied when we are *given* that N is nonsensical, while the various criteria of verifiability have been devised for just those cases where it is not given, but we wish to determine whether or not N is significant.

The correct solution to the problem he raises lies simply in pointing out that nothing is verifiable in principle, unless there are circumstances in which it would actually be verified. But there are no conceivable circumstances under which $(S \lor N) \sim S$ could be verified since this would require that both S and $\sim S$ were verified concurrently. $(S \lor N) \sim S$ is therefore unverifiable. This remains a fact to which the separate verifiability of $S \lor N$ and $\sim S$ is utterly irrelevant.

To the second objection, the answer is that the principle, according to which a statement is confirmable (is verifiable) if and only if circumstances are describable under which it would be confirmed, is sufficient to provide us with the criterion which distinguishes clearly between what is and what is not verifiable. Naturally, however, as long as we have misconceptions as to the nature of confirmation and are not clear under what conditions a statement may be said to have been confirmed, we shall not be able to obtain a clear view of the concept of confirmability either.

As is known, Ayer modified his criterion as a result of Berlin's criticism. His modified version was, however, attacked by Church.

[1] 'Verifiability in Principle', *Proceedings of the Aristotelian Society,* xxxix (1939), pp. 225–8.

Nidditch revised Ayer's new criterion, but Nidditch's suggestion was faulty by Scheffler, and so on.[4] I submit that all these noted thinkers committed one and the same error, which we are now in a position to see: before tackling the problem of confirmability, they neglected to make sure that they had a firm grip on the concept of confirmation, and in particular to note that there are two concepts of confirmation, the relative and the absolute. Once this is made clear, then it must be obvious to anyone that the possession of empirical significance depends on whether there are circumstances in which the statement in question would be regarded as confirmed in an absolute sense. A statement which is confirmable only relative to theories that would not under any circumstances be acceptable and thus could never acquire any credibility is not empirically significant.

It often happens in philosophy that the first, immediate, commonsense reaction to an issue turns out eventually to have contained more than just a grain of truth. The subsequent debate, although much of it takes us further away from the correct standpoint we were at in the first place, forces us to revise our original ideas and give a more refined version of the initial solution to the problem posed. Ayer's very first criterion turns out in essence to have been the correct one, with the crucial proviso added that a statement satisfying it is to be regarded as verified relative to the theory formed by the auxiliary premisses which are required to be conjoined with that statement to yield the observation sentence. Whether or not such verification confers singificance depends on whether such a theory would, under any circumstances, be regarded as acceptable.

Thus stated, the criterion will not be found damaged by Berlin's point. Indeed, no matter what N stands for, N and $N \supset O$ logically imply O and thus N is confirmed relative to the theory which consists of $N \supset O$. But then, of course, the same O confirms $\sim N$ too, relative to the theory which consists of $\sim N \supset O$. As there is nothing to choose between these theories, neither N nor $\sim N$ receives any absolute confirmation from O. For this reason, it seems that 'the Absolute is lazy' would, under no circumstances, acquire credibility and is thus devoid of significance. On the other hand, the statement 'Caloric fluid flows from A to B' is not completely devoid of empirical

[1] I. Scheffler, *The Anatomy of Inquiry* (New York, 1963), pp. 150–4.

significance, but is so only relative to present-day theories. Relative to the physics of 150 years ago, it was confirmed by the observation that the temperature of *A* decreased while that of *B* increased at an appropriate rate.

(5) *The Criterion of Confirmability*

To sum up let me state our criterion of confirmation formally:

> *S* is confirmed relative to *T*, if in conjunction with *T* it non-redundantly entails an established observation-statement.

Note that we are disregarding here the existence of statistical theories, i.e. theories which do not entail but merely render probable certain observation statements. The term 'non-redundantly' has been inserted in order to exclude statements from being confirmed, which together with *T* entail no more observation statements than *T* on its own.

This criterion, as it stands, still excludes many conditional statements rightly regarded as confirmed and therefore, has to be relaxed further. Conditionals of the form 'If *A* were the case then *C* would be the case' which, as is well known, are not equivalent to $A \supset C$, and hence whose truth values are not determined by the truth values of *A* and *C*, are, in general, confirmed by the fact that a set of confirmed statements (restricted in a number of formal ways, i.e. they must not contain $\sim A$, etc.) implies $A \supset C$. Thus the widely held proposition that, were space travel possible at very high speeds for long periods of time, then travellers returning to the earth would appear to have aged less than their earth-bound contemporaries, is regarded as fairly credible. But this is so not because, by itself or in combination with anything else, the proposition yields an established observation-statement, but rather because the material implication 'If anyone travels at high speed then his aging process is retarded' is entailed by a set of statements (in this case a set which constitutes a part of the Special Theory of Relativity) which are justifiably regarded as confirmed. Thus we need disjunctively to add a consequence condition to our criterion. *S* is confirmed relative to *T* either if it satisfies the criterion as above, or if it satisfies the following:

S follows from a set of statements belonging to *T*. In the particular case in which *S* is of the form $A \supset C$, the counter-factual in which *A* is the antecedent and *C* the consequent is regarded as confirmed relative to *T*.

As soon as we have obtained the criterion for testing whether *S* is *confirmed*, the criterion to determine whether *S* is *confirmable* follows: *S* is confirmable if a situation is describable in which we would reasonably subscribe to a theory relative to which *S* is confirmed. *S* is altogether unconfirmable if no circumstances, however strange and remote, are conceivable under which an acceptable theory can be suggested in the context of which *S* would receive confirmation.

(6) *The Cancellation of Symmetrical Contraries*

In concluding this chapter it is appropriate to devote a brief discussion to a very simple and obvious principle we have had occasion twice to employ in this chapter. We first employed it on page 51 in answering Hempel's objection to his own converse-consequence condition. We said that since an arbitrary *b* is just as much entailed by *b.h* as by *b.~h*, *b*'s relation to *h* and ~*h* is symmetrical; hence its effect on one of them is cancelled by its effect on the other and ultimately neither *h* nor ~*h* is absolutely confirmed (in the sense that neither of them is actually rendered credible) by it. I do not believe this claim needs to be defended; when ~*h* is just as much confirmed as is *h* it should be clear from the very meaning of the notion of evidential support that the ultimate effect of these confirmations amounts to nil.

Another argument that an arbitrary *b* does not render just any *h* credible is the following: ~*b* is entailed by ~*b.h* just as much as is *b* by *b.h*. Thus we see that *b* and ~*b* are symmetrically related to *h*; hence their implications for it mutually cancel one another. Once more the reason is obvious. When some hypothesis *h* is made credible on the basis of observation *b* this is because *h* is a part of, or constitutes by itself, the best account of *b*. By '*h* accounts for *b*' we mean that *h* provides a reason why *b* and not ~*b* is the case. But an *h* which would just as well account for ~*b*, if that were the case, is not a good account of either.

The outcome of these considerations is the conclusion that Hempel may safely maintain his converse-consequence condition as long as he does so in conjunction with the following general principle about confirmation:

> If h can be shown to be confirmed by b and in exactly the same way it can be shown that $\sim h$ is confirmed by b then the joint effect of these confirmations is nil.

By 'exactly the same way' of course I mean that all we have to do is substitute $\sim h$ for h. The other principle about confirmation is obviously the following:

> If h can be shown to be confirmed by b and in exactly the same way h can also be shown to be confirmed by $\sim b$ then the joint effect of these confirmations is nil.

The second time we employed the principle was in defending our criterion of confirmability against Berlin's criticism. Here again we pointed out that since the contradictories N and $\sim N$ are symmetrically related to O, the effect of O on N is cancelled by its effect on $\sim N$. It follows then from the first principle just enunicated that O, if actually obtained, would not render either N or $\sim N$ credible, hence the possibility of O obtaining does not render N or $\sim N$ significant.

It seems to me that the principle of the cancellation of symmetrical contraries, inspite of its transparency, is worthy of attention, for it may have numerous applications. Here I shall offer one more important example where it may be applied to solve some difficulties which have puzzled a number of philosophers for the last few years. The example concerns objections raised against Hempel's well-known account of what constitutes an explanation. According to Hempel[1]

T and C constitute a potential explanans for a singular sentence E only if

(1) T is essentially generalized and C is singular

(2) E is derivable from T and C jointly but not from C alone and T and C constitute explanations for E if and only if

(1) (T, C) is a potential explanans for E

(2) T is a theory and C is true.[2]

---

[1] *Aspects of Scientific Explanation* (New York, 1965), p. 273.

[2] The actual account of Hempel contains one more condition but it need not concern us here. Nor do we need to know the exact meaning of every technical term expect to note that 'T is a theory' entails 'T is true'.

Against this he himself proposes the following objection:

Let $T_1 = (x) (Px \supset Qx)$, $C_1 = Pa$ & Rab and $E_1 = Qa$ & Rab. Then if T_1 and C_1 are true, they fulfil the conditions which render them a legitimate explanans. This however is unacceptable since we would be explaining E_1 partially by itself saying that the reason why Rab is true is because Rab is true.

It may seem however that the difficulty is not too great. All we have to do is to add to the conditions which render T & C a legitimate explanans the condition that C and E must not have a common consequent. This will do what is required in our case, since C_1 and E_1 have a common consequent, namely Rab, and this rules out C_1 from constituting a part of the explanans.

Surprizingly enough Hempel shows that we cannot have such a restriction. For let $T_2 = (x) (Px \supset Qx)$ and $C_2 = Pa$; these are considered to be the paradigm of what constitutes a proper explanation of $E_2 = Qa$. It is to be noted however that Pa is logically equivalent to $(Pa \lor Qa)$ & $(Pa \lor \sim Qa)$ and Qa is logically equivalent to $(Pa \lor Qa)$ & $(\sim Pa \lor Qa)$. Thus C_2 and E_2 too have a common consequent, namely $(Pa \lor Qa)$ yet by no means do we wish to rule out C_2 from constituting a part of the explanans. We are thus compelled to say that in a proper explanation C and E are permitted to have a common consequent. How then do we account for the fact that C_1 must not be joined with T_1 to explain E_1?

Hempel finds no answer to this question and concludes by saying that our inability to offer a general criterion whereby T_2 & C_2 is a legitimate explanation of E_2 while T_1 & C_1 is not a legitimate explanation of E_1 suggests that there may not be a sharp boundary separating permissible and non-permissible self-explanations. But this is most distrubing. It is after all immediately evident that in the case of T_1 & C_1 we have an illegitimate self-explanation of E_1, and it is also unquestionably evident that in the case of T_2, C_2 and E_2 we have no such thing, yet we are incapable of saying anything about why these obviously different cases are in fact different.

Another well known objection to Hempel's criterion of what constitutes an explanation is raised by Eberle, Kaplan, and Montague.[1] They claim that on Hempel's criterion any theory yields an

[1] Op. cit., p. 294.

explanation for any particular fact and of course a criterion which permits anything to explain everything cannot be an adequate criterion. Let $T_3 = (x)Fx$ and $E_3 = Ha$. Obviously $T' = (x)(y)(Fx \vee \sim Gy \vee Hy)$ is implied by T_3 and therefore is true. Clearly also $C_3 = (\sim Fb.Ga) \vee Ha$, which is implied by E_3, is true. But $T' \& C_3 \rightarrow Ha$ and therefore $T_3 \& C_3 \rightarrow E_3$. But T_3 was just any theory and E_3 any explanandum, yet we have found that T_3 inevitably explains E_3.

I suggest that both these objections can be met by the application of the principle of the cancellation of symmetrical contraries, but before demonstrating this let me make some preliminary remarks, Suppose someone undertook to explain why entropy always increased by saying that it was God who wanted entropy to increase. It is obvious that even someone who firmly believed in God, and hence believed that it must be true that God wants entropy to increase, would not find that he was provided with the slightest insight into why entropy increases. Why not? Some might want to suggest that one can never explain anything by invoking God. This is wrong. It may be that no scientific explanation should make reference to God, but it is not true that no explanation in terms of Divine goals and wishes can provide any understanding. Suppose it were shown that widely accepted theological principles implied that God wishes entropy to increase. In this case theologians, who were satisfied that the existence of the implication had been demonstrated, would find that considerable illumination had been provided why entropy always increases. Why is it then that when the proposition that God wants entropy to increase is not derived independently, but is known only to be true from the fact that entropy increases, then even people who regard theological truth to be the most precious do not find the proposition to have explanatory power?

The answer touches upon the most crucial feature of explanation, namely that when we have an explanation of E then essentially we have been given a reason why E should hold rather than its contrary. This implies that whenever it is explained satisfactorily why E is the case then we know that it would have appeared anomolous and inexplicable should $\sim E$ have been found to be the case. Consequently, we must conclude that we do not really have an explanation of E, if E is true and we seem to be able to explain it, but it can also be shown that, were the world no different from what it is except that $\sim E$ were true, then we should seem to have just as much an explanation of why $\sim E$ is true. The proper thing to say under these circumstances is that we have premises which tend to explain why E is true when E is true, and premises which tend to explain why $\sim E$ is true when $\sim E$ is true, but that we have no actual explanation for anything.

When a theologian is given independent theological reasons which imply that entropy should increase then he feels he has an explanation why entropy increases; for in the light of these reasons he would find it inexplicable should it be the case that entropy always decreased. But when it is said that God wills that entropy should increase only because it is known that in fact entropy increases then there is no real explanation provided, since if it were the case that entropy decreased we should seem to have just as much of an explanation for the decrease of entropy as we had for its increase.

The above example is an application of the principle of the cancellation of symmetrical contraries. If an explanandum E and its contrary are symmetrical with respect to their explainability, that is, if we seem to be able to explain why E if E is true but also why $\sim E$ if the world is exactly the same except that $\sim E$ is true (and all that is implied by $\sim E$), then we have no explanation why E is true when E is true nor why $\sim E$ is true if $\sim E$ is true.

It is most natural therefore to modify Hempel's criterion by saying that his criterion determines under what conditions T and C tend to explain E. T and C actually explain E only if there is no violation of the principle of the cancellation of symmetrical contraries.

We have now a complete solution to the difficulties raised before. T_1 and C_1 logically imply E_1 and therefore tend to explain it. But if we left the world as it was, except that instead of Qa & Rab being true we let Qa & $\sim Rab$ be true, then of course $T_1 = (x)(Pa \supset Qa)$ would remain true but instead of C_1 we should now have it that $C_1 = Pa$ & $\sim Rab$ must be true. But T_1 and C_1 logically imply Qa & $\sim Rab$ no less than T_1 and C_1 implied E; and hence T_1 & C_1 tends to explain the contrary of E when the latter is true, just as much as T_1 & C_1 tends to explain E when E is true. On the other hand in the case of T_2, C_2, and E_2 we do have an actual explanation. For if the world remained unchanged except that $\sim Qa$ rather than E_2 were true this would not affect the·truth values of T_2 or C_2 and we could not derive $\sim Qa$, which is the contradictory of E_2, from T_2 and C_2.

The same considerations apply to the objections rasied by Eberle and his collaborators. Suppose Ha is true. Then, as they have shown, Ha seems explainable with the aid of $(x)Fx$. Suppose however that Ha is not true. Obviously $(x)Fx$ entails $T'' = (x)(y)(Fx \lor \sim Gy \lor \sim Hy)$, and $\sim Ha$ entails $C' = (\sim Fb.Ga) \lor \sim Ha$, which is therefore now true. But T'' & C' entails $\sim Ha$ and therefore tends to explain it. What we have seen then is that if Ha is true we seem to have an explanation why Ha is true, but if the world remains unchanged except that $\sim Ha$ is true we seem to have no less an explanation why $\sim Ha$ is true. It is not the case therefore that $(x)Fx$ actually explains Ha. Given the amended version of Hempel's criterion, T and C only explain E if there is no violation of the principle of the cancellation of symmetrical contraries, and thus Eberle et al have shown only that any theory tends to explain everything, but not that it actually explains it.

Although Hempel's views have been subjected to much criticism, most philosophers agree that they are important. Hence our ability to amend his criterion, in such a way that it escapes two very serious objections, is of value. However the significance of what has been said is not limited to Hempel. No matter what view of explanation we may subscribe to, the principle of the cancellation of symmetrical contraries applies to it. Everyone will agree that an essential part of explaining E consists in showing that $\sim E$ would be inexplicable. Consequently, if it may appear that we have produced an explanation why E, but it can be demonstrated that, were the world to remain unchanged except that E were false, we would seem equally well able to explain that too, then on no view do we have an actual explanation of E.

CHAPTER IV # What Logically Cannot be Confirmed

(1) *Grades of Significance*

One of the consequences of accepting our criterion of confirmability seems to be that we should allow various grades of significance. A statement may be confirmed relative to theories which we do not accept but which are not inconsistent with those we do accept. Such a statement though neither confirmed nor disconfirmed is highly significant. Below it in significance are those statements which are confirmable relative only to theories which are incompatible with those we currently hold. Such statements would be actually confirmed if the world were different from what we at present believe it to be, a world in which theories we now accept would be rejected. The significance of such statements varies with the extent to which the world would have to be altered in order that they could become confirmed. Devoid of all significance are statements with respect to which one is unable to suggest any coherent theory which could be acceptable in any logically possible universe in the context of which that statement could receive confirmation.

As an illustration consider the following three questions:
   (i) Is there life in other solar systems?
   (ii) Did two distant events occur simultaneously?
   (iii) Do molecules trust or fear each other?

In our present state of knowledge no answer can be provided to (i). However it is reasonable to assume that an answer to question (i) is confirmable relative to a theory which would be an extension of our theories currently held. On the other hand an answer to (ii) would only be confirmable relative to a theory which is incompatible with present-day theories (i.e. a theory according to which there are instantaneously transmitted signals).

How about an answer to (iii)? We know that little ingenuity is required for the construction of theories relative to which anything might be confirmed. However, according to our criterion it is not sufficient merely to produce a set of auxiliary premises in conjunction with which an answer to (iii) will imply one or more observation statements. The crucial question which would remain is whether the set so constructed represents the best available theory accounting for the observations referred to by those statements. Even if we choose observations not yet accounted for by any of the theories currently maintained, the arbitrarily constructed theory will not generally be superior to the set of observational reports by themselves. These reports will equal our so-called theory in empirical scope and surpass it in economy. As long as one cannot suggest a theory which may turn out to be acceptable in certain coherently statable circumstances and relative to which an answer to (iii) would be confirmed, any such answer may be regarded in principle as unconfirmable and (iii) will be regarded as being absolutely devoid of cognitive significance.

But the most extreme case is even further removed from confirmability. There are sentences for which we have positive and conclusive proof that they cannot be confirmed as being true or false. An example is S_1: The proposition now being asserted is false. S_1 gives rise to what is known as the Liar's Paradox. If S_1 is true then it may be false, and if it is false then it must be true. Thus we have conclusive evidence that S_1 cannot be confirmed as true nor can it be confirmed as false. Consequently it must be regarded meaningless.

What I have just said runs counter to the received view.[1] The received view has been that the meaninglessness of S_1 arises not out of the fact that it is an extreme instance of an unconfirmable sentence, but from its belonging to a class of expressions marked by a special structure. S_1 is rendered meaningless by its very form; S_1 is a self-referring expression and this disqualifies it from being capable of making any assertions.

---

[1] What I call here the 'received view' has been most succinctly put by L. Wittgenstein in his *Tractatus Logico Philosophicus*, 3.332 'No proposition can make a statement about itself, because a propositional sign cannot be contained in itself.'

The view that self-reference implies meaninglessness has been challenged before. Let me begin by examining the views of one known philosopher who has held that self-reference and meaninglessness do not necessarily go together. Following it I shall give my reasons for assigning S_1 to the more inclusive category of meaningless sentences.

(2) *Popper on Self-Reference*

Popper objects to the received view on the nature of self-referential sentences and holds they are not in all cases devoid of meaning. He advances his view in a Socratic dialogue entitled 'Self-Reference and Meaning in Ordinary Language'.[1] His essay makes delightful reading; however, from a logical point of view, it is surprising to see on what loose arguments he proposes to establish his case. A defender of the orthodox view would find very little difficulty in rebutting each point made by Popper. This seems a pity, for, as I have said, I believe the general sentiments underlying the paper are commendable: the received view ought to be challenged.

Popper's line of attack is to cite counter-examples to the rule that self-referring sentences are always meaningless and finally to proceed to demonstrate that the solution to the Liar's Paradox based on this rule anyhow fails.

Let us first look at the alleged demonstration of the inadequacy of the traditional solution to the Liar's Paradox. What Popper has to say amounts to the following: suppose someone utters S_1: 'The proposition now being asserted is false.' This raises the ancient paradox that if S_1 conveys a true proposition then it must be conveying a false proposition and vice versa. It has been claimed that we can avoid the paradox by simply declaring S_1 to be devoid of all meaning. But, says Popper, this merely shifts the difficulty. Meaningless utterances convey neither true nor false propositions. It is therefore a false claim which attributes falsehood to something devoid of meaning. Philosophers have declared S_1 meaningless; hence to claim that S_1 expresses a falsehood is to make a false claim. But

---

[1] First published in *Mind*, lxiii (1954), pp. 162–9; subsequently reprinted in Popper's *Conjectures and Refutations* (New York, 1968). Page references are to the latter.

it is this very claim that S_1 is being employed to express. We are forced to conclude, therefore, that S_1 is being used to express a falsehood. This result is bad enough in itself. The situation is worse than this, however, for as we very well know if S_1 conveys a false proposition it must be conveying a true proposition; thus, we have the old paradox back with us again.

It is not difficult to point out where Popper has gone seriously wrong. Once we agree that S_1, in spite of whatever it may appear to mean, is devoid of all meaning, the old paradox cannot be resuscitated. For, if S_1 is meaningless, then it asserts nothing, conveys no proposition, carries no claim. To claim that S_1 conveys a false proposition is indeed to make a false claim, but S_1 has not been used to make such a claim; S_1 cannot be used to make such a claim since it is meaningless.

Popper seems to fare even worse when it comes to the counter-examples he produces to show the inadequacy of the orthodox view. One of the these is put forward in the following manner:

Socrates	Could you produce an example of a self-referring assertion which is empirically true?
Theaetetus:	....
Socrates:	I could not hear what you were saying Theaetetus. Please repeat it a little louder. My hearing is no longer what it used to be.
Theaetetus:	I said 'I am now speaking so softly that dear old Socrates cannot make out what I am saying'.
Socrates:	I like this example; and I cannot deny that when you were speaking so softly, you were speaking truthfully. Nor can I deny the empirical character of this truth; for had my ears been younger it would have turned out an untruth. (p. 306.)

The immediate reaction of some readers might be to conclude that the present argument collapses for exactly the same reason as the previous one. It is simply not the case—it might be said—that when

Theaetetus spoke softly he spoke the truth. Admittedly a proposition has to be regarded as true if it corresponds to facts, and it is a fact that Socrates could not hear what Theaetetus was saying. But no facts can correspond to the proposition asserted by Theaetetus' softly spoken utterance, nor, indeed, can any counter it, since no proposition was asserted by Theaetetus. All self-referring utterances are meaningless and Theaetetus' utterance was self-referring.

This, however, would not destroy Popper's case. He could argue, not entirely without justification, that such a conclusion would be based on arbitrary presuppositions. Naturally, if we dogmatically decree that all self-referring utterances are meaningless, then it follows that Theaetetus has said nothing, and, *ipso facto*, the truth or falsity of what he said does not arise. But after all, the very decision to rule that all self-referring utterances are meaningless is now under review. Is it a reasonable decision? Popper seems to have shown that it is not. He has produced an example where no room for uncertainty would seem to exist for anyone, regarding the question what are the relevant facts which determine the truth value of what has been said. If it is a fact that Socrates could not hear Theaetetus speaking, then everyone, unless he feels compelled to protect a special dogma about self-reference, will agree that the facts correspond to what Theaetetus said, and hence that he spoke truly. On the other hand, if Theaetetus' utterance was audible to Socrates, then that utterance conveyed a falsehood. Popper's attack here differs from his other one concerning S_1. There his move was to allow us to declare the utterance meaningless and then to claim to have demonstrated that this at once leads to the attaching of falsity to the proposition conveyed by S_1. In that demonstration, he failed. Here, however, he questions the reasonableness of declaring the self-referring utterance as devoid of meaning in the first place. He seems to have raised a valid question.

Indeed, Theaetetus' utterance is meaningful, but it proves nothing. Surely Popper cannot fail to acknowledge the distinction between that which is being asserted and that through which an assertion is being made. The former is normally called a proposition; the latter a sentence. What we hear or fail to hear, just as what we are able to read, is not a proposition to which truth value attaches. It is rather the physical vehicle, such as a combination of sounds or a collection of marks on a paper, through which a proposition is supposedly conveyed, i.e. a sentence. Those who insist that self-referring sentences do not succeed in conveying propositions are concerned with the kind of sentence which is employed to convey a proposition purporting to refer to that very proposition itself. The sentence voiced by Theaetetus clearly does not belong to this category. The proposition he has asserted does not refer to itself but to the sentence conveying it. Everybody agrees that there is nothing wrong with this kind of self-reference. There are innumerably many examples showing this, e.g. 'This sentence is. . .

  (i) in English
 (ii) written in longhand. . . on a piece of paper
(iii) uttered on a Monday. . . in a room'

Another example of Popper concerns sentences referring to themselves not directly but via each other; that is, the first sentence refers to the second where the second refers to the first. Such sentences are also commonly regarded as not succeeding in conveying a proposition. A well-known example is 'S_2: The next sentence conveys a true proposition', 'S_3: The previous sentence expressed a false proposition'. S_2 and S_3 seem to create a paradox, but the paradox disappears, it is claimed, as soon as we realize that S_2 and S_3 are meaningless because of self-referring. For we cannot decide the truth value of P_2 (the proposition purporting to be expressed by S_2) until we decide the truth value of P_3 which in turn depends on the truth value of P_2. Popper attempts to show that such sentences may nevertheless succeed in expressing propositions:

Theaetetus:	The very next question which I am going to ask you is an extraordinary one, although expressed in perfectly ordinary language.
Socrates:	There is no need to warn me. I am all ears.
Theaetetus:	What did I say between your last two interruptions, Socrates? (p. 304.)

In the present case Theaetetus' first sentence referred to the last and his last sentence to the first yet it would be most unreasonable to rule them out as meaningless. But this example is just as bad as the previous one for it is perfectly clear that Theaetetus has not uttered a self-referring sentence of a sort which has ever been ruled out as illegitimate. His second sentence, which expresses a question, has an established meaning entirely independent of the meaning of the first sentence. Whatever has been conveyed or has not been conveyed by the first sentence, Theaetetus is now asking to have it repeated. Nor is there any problem with the first sentence. In employing the term 'extraordinary' Theaetetus presumably intended to convey the proposition that his next sentence was going to be self-referring. This, however, turns out not to be the case, as we have just seen; therefore we conclude that his first sentence conveyed a false proposition.

Finally, Popper's general conclusion, that self-referring sentences are not as a rule meaningless but that if they lead to paradoxes we must avoid them, will not satisfy many. The less tolerant reader may well be tempted to ask whether this advice is meant as a general short cut to the solution of all sorts of philosophical problems: all talk which is liable to give rise to perplexities should be avoided. But the more sympathetic reader will assume that what Popper actually had in mind was that, even though there are many self-referring sentences which are free from blemish, those which give rise to paradoxes are to be regarded as constituting non-permissible constructions. They must be avoided then, not because we are otherwise faced with a perplexing situation, but because they are not legitimate sentences of the language.

But this does not get us much further. We need something better than an *ad hoc* ruling that certain self-referring sentences, namely those which otherwise would give rise to intolerable paradoxes, are to be treated as ill-formed sentences. We need a general theory of meaning which will entail among many other things that these troublesome expressions cannot convey any propositions.

There is also another even more important objection to the way Popper intended to leave things. No provisions have been made for disqualifying 'S_1* = The proposition now being asserted is true'. It is quite obvious that a theory of ordinary discourse which allows S_1* to feature as a well-formed significant sentence, is unsatisfactory.

For what sort of significance might S_1^* have? It makes absolutely no difference whether it has been uttered or not; nothing can be derived from it, it introduces no information and there is no way to appraise whether it has conveyed a truth or falsehood, nor could it of course be construed as conveying a value judgement, command, or apology.

Some may perhaps be tempted to claim that provision for the disqualification of S_1^* has been made as soon as S_1 has been disqualified, since the negation of an ill-formed sentence is itself ill formed. This obviously would be a mistake. The proposition expressed by S_1^*—if there were such—is not the contradictory of what S_1 purports to asset since it 'affirms' P_1^* and not P_1.

I have devoted a considerable amount of time to the examination of Popper's views on self-reference. Now it must be admitted that his treatment is by no means the most elaborate or profound or instructive. Dozens of articles have been written on the topic by logicians whose approach has been far more careful and rigorous and who have made much more substantial contributions to the illumination of the problem.[1] I have nevertheless concentrated on the views of Popper because in one aspect—an aspect which is important for my purposes—these views are unique. To my knowledge he is the only philosopher to suggest that the paradoxes are not necessarily the result of a logical flaw common to all those sentences which gives rise to them and that we need not expect to discover anything common in the logical structure of all these troublesome expressions.

Popper, however, as we have seen, unfortunately did not provide sufficient reasons for rejecting the orthodox view. Also, he went too far in maintaining that one cannot say anything more about the paradoxes than that they are paradoxical and must be avoided. In what follows I shall try first to establish more decisively the untenability of the orthodox view through what I hope will be genuine counter-examples. Next I shall conclude with Popper that indeed we may not discover anything in common in the form of all those sentences which give rise to paradoxes. After all we have not

[1] See for example *The Paradox of the Liar,* ed. R. L. Martin (New Haven, Conn., 1970), which contains a number of illuminating papers on the topic.

discovered there to be anything in common in the form of empirically significant sentences like 'All ravens are black', 'Newton's laws govern the motion of celestrial bodies', and so on, on the one hand, nor have we discovered a common logical structure among sentences like 'The Absolute is lazy', 'Entelechy tends to intensify', and others which are devoid of all significance, on the other. Yet by the application of a general criterion that we have constructed (pp. 57–8) we can recognize the former kind of sentences as significant and the latter as nonsensical. I claim that by the application of a principle which implies this very same general criterion, and without necessarily discovering a logical peculiarity shared by all those sentences which gave rise to paradoxes such as self-reference or some other structural defect, we can recognize these sentences as meaningless and hence avoid the paradoxes.

(3) *The Elimination of Self-Reference*

Suppose I assert the following:

P: Object O is red.

Q: If object O is any *other* colour than red, then the proposition correctly stating O's colour is not strictly implied by anything I have said (including what I am saying now).

Q is obviously self-referential and the self-reference here is made not to the physical casing but to the proposition encased, since the particular which is capable of entering into the relationship of strict implication is a proposition and not the sentence expressing that proposition. At the same time Q is clearly meaningful and expresses a proposition which is true and will universally be judged true by all persons without prior commitment to the view that all self-referring utterances must be deemed meaningless.

The meaningfulness of Q however does not show conclusively the correctness of the view I am advocating. Those who subscribe to the received view will not necessarily regard Q as constituting a decisive counter-example to their position. Genuinely self-referring expressions, it might be maintained, never succeed in conveying any meaning; Q, however, is not ineradicably self-referring. This can easily be seen once we consider the two logical equivalences to which the definitions of P and Q give rise:

$P{\leftrightarrow}rO.(f){\sim}(fO.f{\neq}r)$ (i)

(where 'f' ranges over colour-predicates and on the assumption that O can have no more than one colour)

$Q{\leftrightarrow}(f)[(fO.f{\neq}r){\supset}{\sim}(P.Q{\rightarrow}fO)]$ (ii)

$P.Q{\leftrightarrow}rO.(f)\langle{\sim}(fO.f{\neq}r).[(fO.f{\neq}r){\supset}{\sim}(P.Q{\rightarrow}fO)]\rangle$

                                (conjoining (i) and (ii))

$P.Q{\leftrightarrow}rO.(f){\sim}(fO.f{\neq}r)$ (since ${\sim}A.(A{\supset}B){\leftrightarrow}{\sim}A$)

$P.Q{\leftrightarrow}P$

Substituting on the basis of this P for $P.Q$ in (ii), we have

$Q{\leftrightarrow}(f)[(fO.f{\neq}r){\supset}{\sim}(P{\rightarrow}fO)]$

which no longer contains Q.

Suppose that I assert P in conjunction not with Q but with R:

R: If object O has any colour at all, then the proposition cor-
    rectly stating O's colour is not strictly implied by anything I
    have said (including what I am saying now).

Since P is true only if rO holds, in which case R is false, P and R are inconsistent. Consequently the conjunction P and R implies anything; in other words $(f)(P.R{\rightarrow}fO)$; and since R denies this, R is false as long as O has any colour. Thus R is logically equivalent to ${\sim}(\exists f)fO$ which is not a self-referring expression.

The same can be obtained formally by employing the logical equivalence arising out of the definition of R:

$R{\leftrightarrow}(f)(fO{\supset}{\sim}(P.R{\rightarrow}fO)]$ (iii)

$P.R{\leftrightarrow}rO.(f)[fO{\supset}{\sim}(P.R{\rightarrow}fO]$ (conjoining (i) and (iii))

$P.R{\rightarrow}rO.[rO{\supset}{\sim}(P.R{\rightarrow}rO)]$ (Universal Instantiation)

$P.R{\rightarrow}{\sim}(P.R{\rightarrow}rO)$ (Modus Ponens)

which shows that $\square{\sim}PR$ since it strictly implies a necessary falsehood. Substituting $2 + 2 = 5$ into (iii) which is logically equivalent to $P.R$ we get:

$R{\leftrightarrow}(f)[fO{\supset}{\sim}(2 + 2 = 5{\rightarrow}fO)$

$R{\leftrightarrow}(f){\sim}fO$ as before.

Thus the meaningfulness of R does not damage the traditional point of view any more than Q.

Now consider however the case in which I assert S in conjunction with P

S: If object O has any colour at all, then the proposition cor-
    rectly stating O's colour is not uniquely strictly implied by

anything I have said (including what I am saying now). Note: p uniquely strictly implies q, or $p \to_u q =_{def} [(p \to q).\sim(p \to \sim q)]$.

I shall show that when P is asserted together with S then a basis is provided for the logical deduction that P is necessarily false. This of course is an absurdity, for why should it make any difference to the truth value of P what else is uttered in conjunction with it? Besides, the truth of P solely depends on whether O is red or is not red, and this is a contingent matter. Thus, if P is true it is contingently so, and if false contingently false. And yet I shall show that $\Box \sim P$ in two steps: (a) showing that $\Box \sim (P.S)$ and (b) showing that S must always be true. But there can be only three cases in which $\Box \sim (P.S)$: (i) P contradicts S, (ii) $\Box \sim S$, and (iii) $\Box \sim P$. The fact that S is always true rules out (i) since O being red is a contingent matter and hence the assertion that it is red need not always be false; (ii) is ruled out also; hence $\Box \sim P$ must be the case:

(a)   (1) ro $(= O$ is red $= P)$ .... Given
      (2) $(f)[fO \supset \sim (P.S \to_u fO)]$ .... Given
      (3) $P.S$ .... Conjunction (1) and (2)
      (4) $rO \supset \sim (P.S \to_u rO)$ .... Univ. Inst. (2)
      (5) $\sim (P.S \to_u rO)$ .... Mod. Pon. (1) and (4)
      (6) $\sim [(P.S \to rO).\sim(P.S \to \sim rO)]$ ..... Definition of $\to_u$ (5)
      (7) $\sim (P.S \to rO) \vee (P.S \to \sim rO)$ ...... De Morgan (6)
      (8) $P.S \to rO$ .... Tautology (Since $P \leftrightarrow rO$)
      (9) $P.S \to \sim rO$ .... Hypot. Syllog. (7) and (8)
   $\therefore$ (10) $\sim rO$ $(= \sim P)$ .... Mod. Pon. (3) and (9)

i.e. $\sim P$ is logically derivable from P and S.
    $\therefore (P.S) \to \sim P$
    $\therefore \Box \sim (P.S)$

(b) We have

    (A) $S \leftrightarrow (f)[fO \supset \sim (P.S \to_u fO)]$

from the definition of S; and since $P.S$ is necessarily false $\sim [(P.S \to_u fO)]$ is true (and in most modal systems necessarily true) since both $(P.S) \to fO$ and $(P.S) \to \sim fO$ are true. Thus the right-hand side of (A) has been shown true. Thus S is true.

How are we then to avoid the absurd result that $\Box \sim P$? The most natural suggestion to make is that the whole derivation is faulty since we have been employing S which was illegitimate, it being a meaningless sentence. S is meaningless since it is self-referring. But this move is no longer available to us since the self-reference is eliminable from S

We have:

(B) $(P.S) \leftrightarrow 2 + 2 = 5$

since $\Box \sim (P.S)$, and all logically false expressions are strictly equivalent. Substituting into (A) on the basis of (B).[1]

(A') $S \leftrightarrow (f)[fO \supset \sim (2 + 2 = 5 \rightarrow_u fO)]$.

Furthermore, if we were to declare S meaningless because self-referring, we would not explain why the illegitimate use of S gives rise just to the absurd result that $\Box \sim P$ and not to something else.

The correct solution of our puzzle is that if P is true then S is meaningless. S is meaningless if P is true because then it can be shown that S can be confirmed as neither true nor false, for if S is true it must be false, and if false it must be true.

Suppose P is true; in other words O is red, or rO. Is S true if rO holds? Suppose it is; then there exists a situation in which P and S are concurrently true. Thus the two are consistent and therefore $(P.S \rightarrow rO).\sim(P.S \rightarrow \sim rO)$. S however denies this and therefore must be false in this case. Thus P and S can never together be true and are therefore logically inconsistent and their conjunction implies anything. Therefore $(P.S \rightarrow rO)$ and also $(P.S \rightarrow \sim rO)$, i.e. $\sim[(P.S \rightarrow rO).\sim (P.S \rightarrow \sim rO)]$, i.e. $\sim(P.S \rightarrow_u rO)$.

Thus it is its complete undecidability which renders S meaningless; the undecidability which is rooted in the impossibility of there being anything that could point more to its having one truth value than the other.

Many logicians might refuse to consider what I have said as amounting to a solution of the paradoxes. If self-reference does indeed not necessarily render a sentence meaningless then the sentences which give rise to the paradoxes must share some other logical feature by virtue of which they are defective: until we have discovered his common feature no insight has been achieved into the nature of paradoxical sentences.

[1] For the 'Rule of the Replaceability of Logical Equivalents' in all modal contexts see C. I. Lewis and C. H. Langford, *Symbolic Logic* (2nd ed., New York, 1959), p. 494

My suggestion can, however, be put in a milder form to which most logicians would have no reason to object. The *reason* why paradoxical sentences are defective may lie in some aspect of their structure. But in order to *know* that these sentences are defective to the extent that they are devoid of all meaning and hence incapable of giving rise to any paradox we need not know what this aspect is. We discover this by the application of the principle which is implied by the criterion of significance developed in the last chapter. A sentence like 'The Absolute is lazy' was seen to be meaningless because, although a so-called theory could be constructed in the context of which it would imply an observation sentence, a theory of exactly the same kind can be constructed in the context of which it implies the denial of that sentence. What we see then is that essentially 'The Absolute is lazy' is completely symmetrical with respect to truth and falsity—there is not the slightest reason to assign one value to it rather than the other, nor can we conceive of any circumstances under which this symmetry would cease. I claim that ultimately the same can be said about a sentence like 'The proposition now being asserted is false' and also about the sentence 'The proposition now being asserted is true' and about all the other sentences of this chapter which are meaningless: no reason can be cited why they should be regarded as having one truth value rather than the other.

If what has been said in the last two chapters is correct then we have achieved a strong vindication of the view which associates significance with confirmability. It has been shown that the principle of confirmability can be defended provided we take into account the crucial fact that individual sentences are confirmed when the theory of which they constitute a part is proved to be the best among all the theories with the same empirical range. We have also seen that our principle of empirical significance forms a part of a wider principle of meaningfulness. This more general principle asserts the only decidable sentences have meaning; that is, only sentences with respect to which one can cite some reason why they should be regarded as having one truth value rather than another.

The criterion of confirmability which we developed in the last chapter can thus be seen to derive from a very general principle of meaningfulness made explicit in this chapter. The theory which associates meaningfulness with verifiability was originally the product of a special approach, called verificationism, upheld by the adherents of logical positivism. The form in which the criterion has here been presented would make it acceptable to a much wider circle than those committed to a special ideology or school of thought. The fact that the criterion can be seen to derive from a very simple and obviously reasonable principle should gain its general acceptance. At the same time it might now appear to have been watered down to such an extent that it has become trivial, mechanically applicable, and incapable of yielding interesting results. That this is not so we shall see in the next two chapters.

CHAPTER V

The Application of
the Confirmability
Criterion (I):

The Separation of
Change and Time

(1) *Time without Change*

The fact that we have in our possession a confirmability (or verifiability) criterion to distinguish between what is empirically significant and what is not does not imply that we can now mechanically
determine, in the case of any given sentence, to which of the two
categories it belongs. Given a sentence, there is no standard way to
find out whether it is confirmable in principle; in fact it may require
a very involved procedure to determine whether or not some fictitious situation, however remote from the prevailing one, does or
does not exist in which the sentence would be confirmed relative
to the most acceptable theory. To illustrate the amount and the
nature of the work that may be required in an individual case let
us carefully consider whether the sentence 'A period of time *t* has
passed during which absolutely nothing happened' should be regarded as meaningful.

Sydney Shoemaker, in an ingenious paper 'Time without Change',[1]
claims that it makes sense to speak of a situation in which the whole
world remains frozen for an extended period, during which absolutely nothing happens except that time passes by. First, he asks us
to consider a world which is divided into three regions of space A, B,
and C. Each of these regions is subject to periods of total freeze
and, of course, there is nothing problematic about this since, when
A is having one of its periods of freeze while B is not, then the inhabitants of B can observe how everything in A comes to a complete

[1] *Journal of Philosophy*, lxvi (1969), pp. 363–81.

standstill and remains so without any movement or change for a given period.

Now past observations have taught the inhabitants of this world that all periods of local freeze are preceded by periods of local sluggishness during which it takes more than the normal amount of effort to move about, and that the duration of this period of sluggishness, in any given region, is always proportional to the length of the period of freeze which follows it there. It has also been confirmed that no period of freeze lasts less than six months. Suppose periods of sluggishness occur simultaneously in A, B, and C. These on the basis of past observations, are supposed to be followed by periods of freeze not shorter than six months and proportional to the length of the periods of sluggishness, even though, of course, such periods will not be observable since they overlap. Thus, on the basis of past observation, the inhabitants of the universe may reasonably conclude that, for a given period, the whole of the universe was in a state of total freeze.

In the case before us then 'T' may be taken to stand for 'Whenever there is a period of sluggishness throughout a given region of space this is always followed by a certain period of total freeze in the same region'; and we also have h: 'The whole universe was in a state of complete freeze for a given period.' It seems then that given b, which in this case stands for all our observations concerning sluggishness and associated phenomena, T is a better way of accounting for b than any other. It may therefore be claimed that as long as no one comes up with a better account of b than T, h is to be regarded as confirmed relative to the most acceptable theory and thus absolutely confirmed. The fact that we were able to describe circumstances under which h would be absolutely confirmed renders h confirmable in principle and thus empirically significant.

There are, however, obvious difficulties. There is of course nothing wrong in showing that an h, previously regarded as unconfirmable in principle, may be confirmed under some strange circumstances nobody has thought of before. But surely not if h is self-contradictory. When h is self-contradictory then the existence of this or that kind of theory and observation is quite irrelevant: nothing can render self-contradictory statements confirmable.

Now there exists a certain well-known and respectable view, according to which time is constituted of physical processes or changes and does not exist apart from the various time-dependent physical parameters. Bertrand Russell is a famous representative of this view. He emphasizes that the relation of moments in time to events which occur at them must not be viewed like pegs on which hats are hung. Hat-pegs continue to exist when the hats are removed from them, but there can be no moments totally devoid of all events. On this view, the reason why we deny that a passage of time of a given length has occurred without being accompanied by any event happening or any change taking place is not because we deem such a claim unverifiable but because we regard it as self-contradictory. Time is constituted of the events occurring in it and has no independent existence apart from them. To claim that time has passed without anything occurring amounts to saying that events have occurred without any events occurring. All efforts to devise means to verify such a claim are certain to fail for nothing will count as a verification of a self-contradictory assertion.

It is possible to reply to this that *h* expresses a self-contradiction only on the presupposition that time without events is non-existent. One should ask, however, how we came to believe this in the first place. It is not unreasonable to claim that the source of this presupposition is the belief that to allow the possibility of changeless intervals is to allow the possibility of something unconfirmable in principle taking place. But given the situation previously described, it should become clear that to postulate changeless intervals is not necessarily to postulate something wholly unconfirmable, and therefore we should embrace an alternative view according to which time has an existence purely of its own.

Let us therefore agree not prejudicially to assume that *h* expresses a self-contradiction and that under the circumstances described *h* is confirmed relative to *T*. The question which still arises is: even under those circumstances is *T* the most acceptable theory? It is after all possible to subscribe to T' which is 'Whenever there is a period of sluggishness throughout a given region of space this is always followed by a certain period of total freeze in the same region except when the sluggishness affects the whole universe.'

It may seem that T' is inferior to T since it introduces an exception to the straightforward rule enunciated by T. To this one may reply that T' introduces the kind of exception with which we are familiar elsewhere. Consider the placing of a weight on the scale of a balance. Putting a weight in one of the dishes of a balance in equilibrium will usually cause that dish to go down. But not always—not if at the same time an equal weight is placed in the other dish. Similarly one might say a period of sluggishness is followed by a period of freeze relative to any region in which no period of sluggishness has occurred. But if a period of sluggishness in region A is 'counterbalanced' by a similar period in B then neither undergoes a freeze relative to the other.

One might attempt to claim on Shoemaker's behalf that T' is defective in that it fails to provide a causal explanation for what is going on. After all, in the case of the balance, although it is true that neither dish descends as a result of a weight being placed in it when a counterweight is placed in other dish, the placing of weights in both dishes is not devoid of all after-effects: tension in the balance arms, for example, is increased. In the situation presented by Shoemaker, if we adhere to the Russellian position, we cannot say that a period of sluggishness throughout the universe brought about a period of changelessness. Thus it seems that the state following a period of universal sluggishness may be indistinguishable from a state not following such a period, which amounts to a violation of the principle that every event has an effect.

However, a Russellian does not have to maintain that a period of sluggishness may occur without its having any after-effects. In a deterministic universe it is indeed required that any state marked by some special property is followed by a state specially marked. A state of sluggishness, we are told, is usually followed by a state of freeze. Shoemaker does not explicitly say this, but one is to assume that a state of freeze is followed by a state which, too, is marked in some special way; for it would amount to a violation of the causal principle if normal states of a given region and states of total freeze of the same region could be succeeded by similar states. Thus, even when a state of sluggishness is not followed by a state of relative freeze, since it has occurred concurrently in all three regions, it still has the effect of bringing about a special state in all those regions, a state associated with a period of post-freeze.

It is clear then that Shoemaker holds the view that, while our access to time is through the various physical processes which occur in it, these processes are merely co-variants of time and do not actually constitute it; time is measured through the various time-dependent quantities but it exists independently of them. While this view is not necessarily wrong, holding it, unfortunately, produces new reasons for supposing that Shoemaker has failed to establish his point through the universe he has created. On the view that, over and above all the events, changes, and processes, there exists also Time as such, it is obvious that two distinct descriptions may be offered of what actually takes place when A is observed to have frozen relative to B. According to one description, all physical processes in A have come to a complete standstill while time itself continues to progress in A at the same rate as in B. According to the second description, all physical processes stop *because* time itself in A comes to a halt and begins to move again only after a certain time has passed in B. Shoemaker has certainly not given any reason why, when region A is observed to undergo a period of freeze, description one is preferable to description two. On the surface, description two might be preferable to description one, since it does not allow the problem of causes acting across a time-gap to arise. When a stone on its flight from X to Z is interrupted at Y because of the freeze, there is really no time interval between its flight from X to Y and Y to Z, at least not in the region in which the process and the freeze have occurred.

If, however, description two is adopted, then we say that whenever a period of sluggishness occurs in region A, while no such period occurs in B, then this is followed by a period of freeze in A, as observed in B, to last an amount of time proportional to the length of the period of sluggishness preceding. This freeze is interpreted as the stoppage of time itself in A for a specified duration in B. It is obvious that it is logically impossible that time should stop in all the regions of the universe concurrently. For to say that time has stopped everywhere throughout the universe is to contradict one-self. The sentence 'Time has stopped' is always elliptical for 'Time has stopped for a duration t', which can express a coherent statement only if the term 'time', at the beginning of the sentence, refers to time in another system than the term 'duration t'', at the end of the sentence, which refers to a time that continues.

We shall not let matters rest here. However, before making any further attempts to invest h with empirical significance, I shall first consider the possible views on the status of 't' as it is employed in physics.

(2) *The Meaning of a 'Time Interval'*

Three different views on the status of 't' seem possible. According to one view, nature consists of a very large number of clocks, each corresponding to some process, and the rate of progress of each can be compared to another, but not to the rate of time itself. For it is not the case that, in addition to and side by side with all these clocks, there exists yet another perfect or ideal clock which may be spoken of as constituting time. 't' represents intervals covered not by time itself, but by the standard we have chosen to measure the rate of all the rest of the clocks.

An alternative view is based on the observation that the standard is not arbitrarily chosen. We could, for instance, opt to take the rotating earth as our standard but only at the price of having to assign systematically to all other processes a specific irregularity in addition to any irregularity they may already possess. We prefer, however, not to assign irregularity to all the various natural processes but assign it rather to one single process, namely, the rotation of the earth, and explain it as being due to the friction of the tides. In this manner, by trying to remove all systematic irregularities through identifying their causes as lying in some specific process, we get closer to reconstructing that ideal process which progresses at a perfectly even rate and which we think of as the progress of time itself.

Russell, in evaluating this argument, points out that to object and say that time can have no rate of progress, since it cannot directly be observed but only reconstructed on the basis of the complex considerations just outlined, would amount to a misunderstanding of the nature of science where we assume the existence of all sorts of entities, events, and processes not directly given to observation. The objection which, however, may validly be levelled against this reconstruction of time, according to Russell, should be based

> on the fact that physics can be interpreted without assuming it. Whenever a body of symbolic propositions which there is reason to accept can be interpreted without inferring such-and-such unobserved entities, the inference from the body of propositions in question to those supposed entities is invalid, since, even if there are no such entities, the body of propositions may be true. It is on this ground, and not merely because 'absolute' time cannot be observed, that Newton was mistaken in inferring it from the law of physics.[1]

It seems indeed very reasonable to say: the tendency of objectify what '*t*' represents and view it as the magnitude of intervals actually described by a process which is the advance of time itself must be resisted. The hypostatization of time in the form of a perfect clock existing side by side with other clocks, and whose rate of progress ultimately determines the rate at which all other natural processes advance, is quite unwarranted. From this, however, it does not follow that we must take the stand that '*t*' signifies nothing in objective reality. A middle course between the two extreme ways of viewing the status of what '*t*' represents would be to say that it serves as our standard of the congruence of non-adjacent temporal intervals.

Let me elaborate. The situation with respect to the congruence of temporal intervals is very similar to the situation which obtains with respect to the more familiar concept of the congruence of spatial intervals. Direct observation of the congruence of spatial intervals can be made only in the special case in which two intervals lie side by side and their extremities are seen to coincide. Distant intervals can only be compared indirectly with the help of certain assumptions. An essential role in such indirect comparisons is played by the principle of simplicity. For example, two non-adjacent spatial intervals through which the round trip of light signals takes equal times will be regarded as congruent. It would, of course, be logically possible to assign different magnitudes to these intervals at

[1] *Human Knowledge: Its Scope and Limit* (London, 1948), p. 286.

the expense of systematically complicating all the laws of physics. We prefer, however, to adopt the principle of maximizing the simplicity of our physics and assuming that the speed of light does not vary with different regions of space.

In the temporal situation, again, only in a very special case can congruence by directly observed: when intervals lie side by side, i.e. when they are co-temporal. For example, the interval constituted by the cooling body's change from temperature O_1 to O_2 will be judged as congruent with the interval constituted by the clock-hand moving from position P_1 to P_2 if the two pairs of events forming the extremities of these intervals are simultaneous.

What about temporally non-adjacent intervals? Instead of saying that such intervals are not comparable, we extend the notion of congruence to them essentially in the same way we do in the spatial case. Once again, we assume that the laws of physics are constant and that they do not vary with different regions of time.

This assumption is, of course, subject to the proviso that there are no special causes operating, making some systems behave differently at different times. In the case of the rotating earth, for example, in order to achieve a simpler physics, we assume the interference of certain specified causes which give rise to a variable period of rotation.

In general, we infer the congruence of two intervals if assuming them to be congruent maximizes the over-all simplicity of the set of all known physical laws. Thus, two subsequent intervals covered by a given process, both of which are measured as of length 't'—where the value of 't' is arrived at in the manner previously described, i.e. through the application of the principle of maximizing simplicity— will be regarded as congruent. Thus, it is by no means assumed that there is an ideal or transcendental master clock which keeps ticking away, each 'tick' marking the end of an interval and inaugurating another one equal in length to the last. No extra unwarranted entities are being postulated. But the series of moments which is our time series is given to us and what we want is to find a way of dividing it into equal intervals, so that within all processes we may be able to distinguish between equal and unequal intervals.

On this account, when the rate of a process is said to be functionally related to 't' in some specific manner, this should not be taken as saying that the process in question advances so much while time advances that much, but merely as specifying the way in which the magnitudes of various intervals constituting the given process are to be related to one another. For example, when it is said that the law of free fall is of the form '$s \propto t^2$',[1] this must not be interpreted as meaning that larger and larger distances, described by the moving particle subjected to the force of gravity, correspond to subsequent equal intervals covered by the perfect clock which keeps the universe's time, but merely as meaning that equal temporal intervals are marked off by the events of the particle reaching points which are increasingly further and further apart.

Naturally, just as we may wish to speak of the way the subsequent distances described by the falling particles are related to one another in terms of the number of unit time intervals corresponding to them, so too we may want to consider that $t \propto \sqrt{s}$, which is the functional relationship in which the number of unit space intervals plays the role of the independent variable. In this case, we are considering the way subsequent temporal intervals are related to one another in terms of the distances described by the falling particle. It may be said that we are considering the rate at which time is progressing in terms of the progress of the particle. This talk seems innocuous enough, as long as it is clearly understood what is meant by it and no attempt is made to hypostatize this progress as being that of an extraneous master clock.

There are thus three different ways of interpreting the variable 't' which ranges over 'time' in the equation used by physicists. These are best summarized, perhaps, in the context of a concrete example. Suppose one day we are able to construct a clock C which will keep perfect time. There are then three different ways of viewing what C is actually doing:

V1.   According to this view, a view which is attacked by Russell, it will be said that clock C is synchronous with time itself. Thus, if the numerals 1, 2, 3, and so on divide the dial of the clock into equal sections, then while the clock hand moves from 1 to

[1] i.e. s varies directly with t^2.

2 and then from 2 to 3 time itself too passes through equal intervals.

V2. This is the view which is at the extreme opposite end to view 1. According to it, all one can say is that it has been found that expressing the rate of all the processes as functionally related to the rate of clock C yields the simplest possible physics. For this reason, we chose clock C as our standard against which to measure the rate of all other clocks. But it makes no sense to say that clock C is really a better clock than any other because its rate is more even. Its rate is objectively no more even than the rate of any other clock, except for the convention which treats it as the standard.

V3. This view stands somewhere midway between view 1 and view 2. According to it, the correct way to describe what C is doing is the following: Let e_1 be the event of C's hand coinciding with numeral 1, e_2 its coinciding with 2, and so on, then the intervals $e_1 - e_2$ and $e_2 - e_3$ and so on are really equal. Clock C may objectively be regarded as superior to other clocks in so far as it is the realization of a system in which some other equal physical intervals, i.e. spatial intervals into which the dial of C is divided, are covered in temporal intervals that are congruent.

It seems that Russell's position is represented by V2, although I am not certain that, if V3 were put to him, he would feel impelled to disagree with it. Newton's position is more likely to be represented by V1 than by V3—but there is some ambiguity in his writings in this regard.

It is most important to realize that the difference between V1 and V3 lies essentially in that, according to V1, the time series is made up basically of a dense set of moments (or instants) to which events may attach themselves. These events are to the moments at which they occur, says Russell, as the hats are to the pegs upon which they are hung. According to V3, however, moments or instants have no independent existence of their own: a moment is to be defined as a set of events of infinitesimal duration. Empty moments or moments unoccupied by any event—unlike empty hat-pegs—by definition do not exist.

The apparent weakness of V1 seems to be that it postulates unnecessarily an extra entity. It need not, of course, be assumed that, according to V1, some material clock exists hidden from us with its wheels and gears grinding away, a clock that is a master clock of the universe, the time shown upon which determines the stages to be reached by all the processes in nature. It is enough that V1 postulates that, in addition to all directly or indirectly recognizable events, there is a dense series of moments, stretches of which constitute intervals of time.

There is, however, reason to be dissatisfied with the picture presented by V2. First of all, it disallows the extension of the notion of congruence to non-adjacent temporal intervals, one which would be a most natural extension. But it will also be found unsatisfactory, at least by some, that processes are related to nothing intrinsically more relevant than to one another and that the rate of one process is determined merely by the rate of another process. No link has been provided, on such a view, which might reasonably be thought of as 'holding together' these processes. Of course, the force of such an objection would not amount to more than, say, the force of the objection which has been levelled on *a priori* grounds against action at a distance. Yet to some, while this objection could not stand up against empirical facts, if there were such, it nevertheless may determine that we choose a different picture, according to which a cause which satisfies us as being rationally capable of determining the rate of processes is, in fact, operative. According to the other two views we have presented, the reason, of course, why the distance fallen by a particle under the force of gravity is such-and-such is not given in terms of something as seemingly unrelated to this distance as the number of particles remaining in a decaying nucleus, or the amount of heat dissipated by a radiating body, or the distance travelled by a light ray, where all these processes begin and end simultaneously. The reason supplied by V1 and V3 is given in terms of a process which constitutes a much more natural candidate for providing such an explanation: the amount of time which elapsed.

(3) *Change in the Rate of Time-Flow*
   and Change in the Rate of Processes

On the analysis of the last section it would seem that V2 is the least plausible view to take on the question of what we are measuring with our clocks. However, as we have seen, this does not force us to accept V1; we have the alternative of subscribing to V3. This does not bring us much closer to our aim which was to invest the statement 'The whole universe was in a state of complete freeze for a given period' with empirical significance. V3 agrees with V2 that there are no eventless moments. The question is: can we describe a logically possible situation in which the theory which subscribed to V1 was the most acceptable theory?

In what follows I shall attempt to show that we can describe such a situation. The adoption of V1 on its own, however, is not sufficient. As we have already pointed out, on this view a period of freeze may be interpreted in two ways and according to one not only events have frozen but time itself has come to a halt, which is not the situation we are after. What we need therefore for our purposes is some means of distinguishing between states of freeze which represent the stoppage of physical processes while time continues in its flow and those which amount to the stoppage of time itself. I shall also attempt to show that it is at least conceivable that circumstances should obtain under which such a distinction can be made.

Suppose there are two regions of space, S_1 and S_2, and in S_2 all processes proceed at half the rate they proceed in S_1. For example when two light signals are simultaneously emitted in the two spaces, the one in S_1 will have covered a distance c while the other in S_2 will have only travelled a distance $\frac{c}{2}$; if two particles are simultaneously released near the surface of earthlike bodies in the two regions of space, the one in S_1 will have fallen a distance of $\frac{1}{2}g$ while its counterpart will have descended to a depth of $\frac{1}{8}g$; when two identical decaying nuclei distintegrate according to the law $n = n_0 e^{-kt}$, then while in the one that is in S_1, $n_0 e^{-k}$ particles remain intact, in its counterpart in S_2, $n_0^{-k/2}$ particles will so remain.

Two explanations are compatible with the observed situation. To see clearly the difference between them, let us write down T, which is the general equation embodying all the laws governing the rate of the various processes there are. Let q_t stand for any quantity which grows or wanes with time, then

$$q_t = a_0 + a_1 t + a_2 t^2 \ldots a t^n \qquad (T)$$

to any desired degree of accuracy.

For example: q_t may stand for the distance travelled by light in a vacuum; to obtain its value, we put all coefficients zero except a_1 which equals c. If q_t stands for the distance fallen by a particle subject to the gravitational pull of an earthlike body, then it is given by T in which we equate all coefficients zero except a_2 which equals $\frac{1}{2}g$. If q_t denotes the number of atoms remaining intact in the decaying substance, then we may obtain this number from T by equating

$$a_0 = 1, a_1 = -K, \ a_2 = \frac{K^2}{2!} \ldots a_n = (-1) n \frac{K n}{n!}$$

Now, according to explanation A, while T yields the value of any quantity which grows or wanes with time in S_1, in S_2 such quantity q_t is given by equation T'_A:

$$q_t = a_0 + \frac{a_2}{2} t + \frac{a_2}{2^2} t^2 + \ldots \frac{a_n}{2^n} t^n \qquad (T'_A)$$

while according to explanation B in S_2, instead of T, (T'_B) applies:

$$q_t = a_0 + a_1 \frac{t}{2} + a_2 (\tfrac{t}{2})^2 + \ldots a_n (\tfrac{t}{2})^n \qquad (T'_B)$$

Equations (T'_A) and (T'_B) are, of course, mathematically equivalent and, for all the different values $a_0, \ldots a_n$ may assume, the two yield the same values for q_t. But there is great difference between the physical explanations the two equations presuppose. Consequently, they imply the existence of different observations with respect to quantities other than q_t. For example, the magnitude of quantities functionally related to some of the coefficients a_1, a_2, etc., but not to t, will be expected to be different on the basis of explanation A from what they would be on the basis of explanation B.

Suppose it is asked: why is it that in S_2 the same particle subject to the same gravitational force falls only a distance of $\frac{1}{8}g$ in one second, while in S_1 it falls a distance $\frac{1}{2}g$? The answer, according to explanation A, is that the particle is not subject to the same gravitational force in S_2 as in S_1. If g stands for the force due to gravity near the surface of an earthlike body in S_1 and g' for that force in S_2, then we see from T'_A that $g = \frac{g'}{4}$. There may be different causes accounting for the fact that $g \neq g'$, one of them being that all bodies when transported from S_1 to S_2 lose 75 per cent of their mass; consequently, the earthlike body in S_2 is only 25 per cent as massive as its counterpart in S_1. According to explanation B, however, $g = g'$ and the two bodies are subject to the same force and indeed they fall equal distances in equal times. But what we must not forget is that the length of time intervals in the two regions of space do not equal one another. While one second passes in S_1, only half of one second passes in S_2 since $\frac{t}{2}$ in S_2 corresponds to t in S_1 as seen from the fact that T'_B, rather than T, yields the correct values then for all q_t.

A great number of observations might point to the correctness of one explanation rather than the other. A straightforward example can very briefly be described, if we assume the caloric theory of heat to be the one adopted by scientists. Suppose it is noticed that, upon crossing the border between the two spaces, all bodies change temperature abruptly: when moving from S_1 to S_2 the absolute temperature of all systems increases four times. According to the caloric theory, $\theta = \frac{\text{amount of caloric fluid}}{\text{mass x specific heat}}$. Taking this into account, we could say that the mass of every body diminishes by 75 per cent as it crosses the border between S_1 and S_2, which according to the formula for temperature implies that its temperature rises four times. The same explanation would then account for the lessening of acceleration of all masses and support explanation A.

Thus, it is logically possible to have a situation in which explanation A is preferable to explanation B. But, of course, according to V2 and V3, explanation A is just not coherent. For in terms of V2 and V3, which claim that time intervals have no independent existence, it just is not possible that all clocks in S_2 should go half the rate they go in S_1, yet the length of time intervals remain the same in both spaces. For on these views over and above all the physical clocks in S_2 there is no additional entity called time. Thus if all the clocks in S_2 which are physically identical to the clocks in S_1 go at half the rate of the latter this cannot be interpreted in any other way but that time itself in S_2 flows at half the rate it flows in S_1. We should, therefore, have strong reason for adopting V1, which is the only view permitting the appropriate explanation of what is going on.

This last important point, that views 2 and 3 cannot accomodate explanation A, may perhaps be more clearly brought out if we consider for a brief moment a very simple world in which there exist no forces or movement, neither heat nor sound, no physical entities of any sort except identical spheres which glow for an instance at regular intervals. Time in this universe could be measured by the number of times any sphere lights up. Let us imagine that this universe consists of S_1 and S_2 and for any period of time during which in S_1 all the spheres light up n times in S_2, they light up $\frac{n}{2}$ times. On V1 the situation could be described in two ways:

(A) Time flows at the same rate throughout space; however in S_2 the spheres emit light at a slower rate than in S_1. The reason for this difference may lie in the fact that the spheres in S_2, though they appear perfectly similar to those in S_1, do after all differ in some yet undiscovered physical aspect, or in that different natural laws govern spaces S_1 and S_2.

(B) The spheres in S_2 twinkle at the same rate as in S_1. This is possible since in S_2 time flows at half the rate it flows in S_1 so the spheres in S_2, though they twinkle at a slower rate relative to the spheres in S_1, relative to their own time system they twinkle at the same rate as do the spheres of S_1 relative to *their* own time system.

On V2 and V3, however, the flow of time is nothing but the process of light emission by the spheres, and this process in S_2 proceeds at half the rate it proceeds in S_1, which is to say that time itself in S_2 proceeds at half of its rate in S_1. Since on V2 and V3 there is nothing over and above the periodic events of glow, explanation A cannot be accommodated on these views (except by adopting the time system of S_1 in S_2 which might be found objectionable on various grounds).

But suppose it were discovered after all that the spheres of S_2 were different from those in S_1 (the latter were all hollow). One would very much want to subscribe to explanation A which is impossible on views 2 and 3. Thus grounds would be provided for adopting V1.

Now let us turn to Shoemaker's problem. Suppose the appropriate circumstances to make us adopt V1 have obtained. Once we have adopted V1 there are no longer any objections against the meaningfulness of maintaining that time has passed without any events occurring. But the question still remains: how would we *know* that when there was a period of freeze in region A what happened was not that time itself had stopped there, but rather that all physical processes had come to a halt? We might have reasonable grounds for maintaining this if things did not come to a complete stop in region A all at once. Imagine that at first processes merely slowed down in A and proceeded at half of the rate in regions B and C, then slowed down to a quarter of the rate, later to one tenth of the rate, until finally they stopped altogether. Suppose also that we had evidence, of the kind described before, that the slow-down in region A should be accounted for by explanation A rather than explanation B, i.e. that physical processes alone, and not time itself, had slowed down. When eventually everything came to a standstill in region A it would be reasonable to maintain that what we had was a culmination of the previous process and that it was not time which had come to a halt in this region. Similarly when the freeze occurs in B and C we might have evidence which renders it reasonable to maintain that it is not time itself that has stopped in these regions. If we combine all this with Shoemaker's story then we may end up with a situation in which we are entitled to claim to have indirect evidence that all processes in the universe come to a standstill while six months of time pass by.

In spite of my lengthy efforts, some may still not be convinced that I have indeed succeeded in constructing a situation in which the assertion that the whole world remained frozen for an extended period, during which nothing happened except that time passed by, would be verified, and thus in showing that the assertion is after all empirically significant. This does not matter so much. Really my main point, a point which I believe I have not failed to demonstrate convincingly, has been the following: we have adopted an exceedingly liberal criterion of empirical significance; all that it requires is that some observation be implied by a significant sentence, no matter what the theory needed to give it context, so long as some circumstances are conceived under which that theory is acceptable. Our criterion is also very simple, much simpler than envisaged by most philosophers. Because of its liberality one might have supposed that it excludes as devoid of significance only those sentences which we could in any case have excluded on other grounds: for example, sentences containing terms which do not stand for anything, like 'The Absolute' or 'entelechy', or sentences in which there is category mixing as in 'The temperature has high velocity'. We see now that this is not obviously so. The sentence we have been considering here is not immediately recognizable as defective, yet on our criterion, unless some complicated manoeuvre of the kind we have just performed succeeds, it may remain devoid of meaning. And surprisingly we have found here also that in spite of its simplicity, when it comes to the application of the criterion to an individual case, it may require very elaborate work to show that a given sentence is or is not empirically significant. The fact that the determination of what is and what is not empirically significant remains a complex task should lend the subject of empirical significance continued interest.

CHAPTER VI

The Application of the Confirmability Criterion (II):

Determinism

(1) *Is the Doctrine of Determinism a Methodological Principle?*

In the previous chapter we investigated the meaningfulness of a sentence which was of no particular importance as such. What did have interest was to see in detail how one applies our criterion to a given sentence. This time we shall consider a sentence the status of which is in itself of great interest. It is moreover a sentence which expresses what is often thought to be a metaphysical doctrine. We shall see that not everything metaphysical is automatically excluded from having significance, by our criterion. A certain clearly defined type of metaphysical statements will be seen as fit to be maintained by the toughest-minded empiricist.

The sentence I propose to investigate is employed in expressing the doctrine of determinism. Most of us feel that the doctrine according to which any given set of physical conditions inevitably gives rise to, or is followed by, another unique set of conditions, whether true or not, is not utterly vacuous. On the contrary, the doctrine seems to us to be of great significance, and its acceptance or rejection has repercussions in fields as far apart as ethics and religion.

Yet it has appeared to many that while various statements asserting that certain specified events are causally determined are amenable to confirmations of different sorts and degrees, the claim that all events are so determined is not confirmable to any extent. Neither on its own nor jointly with any other statement or group of statements does the doctrine seem to entail any observation statement.[1]

---

[1] We may once more be reminded briefly that of course the doctrine together with 'If the doctrine of determinism is true then snow is white' entails 'Snow is white'. This however does not confirm the doctrine at all in an absolute sense since the group of statements entailing it does not constitute an acceptable theory.

Owing to this difficulty some have claimed that the principle of universal causation is to be construed as a recommendation rather than as a cognitive assertion. It has been suggested that the doctrine of determinism constitutes a description not of the world but of a methodological rule scientists should adhere to at all times. The major weakness of any attempt thus to reformulate the principle of universal causation is that people wish to talk about the unreformulated version which, they strongly believe, says something important about the way the universe is constituted, affecting among other things the status of free will.

Here I shall attempt to show that the doctrine of determinism, construed as a straightforward claim about the way things are, has full empirical significance. At the same time I should like to make explicit and clear the sense in which the principle of universal causation differs fundamentally (as we all feel it does differ) from ordinary statements in science.

(2) *Determinism and Cyclicity*

First let me review an interesting idea (I do not know who orginated it) according to which determinism is grounded in experience through its association with a cyclic universe. The assertion that the universe is deterministic has the concrete implication—so it is claimed—that, if it ever reached a state which was identical with a state that had obtained at any time in its past, then the universe would go through eternally recurring cycles henceforward. For, if the universe is deterministic, then once the total state U_0 has been followed by U_1, U_2, ... U_n, U_0 this will happen again and again.

It is by no means clear that this suggestion succeeds in solving the problem of specifying grounds on which to assign empirical significance to determinism. I shall not question the claim that the statement 'The universe is in state U_0 for at least the second time in history' is a confirmable statement (not of course in the sense that it refers to what is directly observable but in the sense that it can be confirmed through observation according to our definition of that term). I think all of us would agree that, if the sole root in observation of a given statement consisted in its entailing a conditional like 'If a substance x is heated to 1000 °C. it will melt', that statement would qualify as confirmable even though no sample of x had ever yet been heated to such a temperature. The heating of a sample x can be brought about. However, there is something quite unique about the statement whose sole root in observation consists in its entailing the conditional 'If the universe is in state U_0 for at least the second time in history, then it will go through recurring cycles eternally'. The circumstances referred to in the antecedent cannot be brought about at will and may never come about.

A more important objection can be brought out in the following way: suppose state U_0 returns for the second time in history. It is claimed that sentient beings inhabiting the universe at some state U_i can become aware of this. But this at once raises the difficulty that their very awareness introduced a factor which distinguishes U_i of this cycle from U_i in the previous cycle. In the second U_i there are creatures who are aware that a state U_i has occurred once before, whereas in the first U_i there could be no such creatures. To remove this difficulty it may perhaps be suggested that if a given state occurs more than once, then the universe goes through an infinite succession of cycles extending eternally into the past and into the future. This removes the objection that U_i in a later cycle cannot be identical with U_i in an earlier cycle, for now it is claimed that people may be justified in maintaining an empirical theory from which it follows that U_i has occurred infinitely many times in the past, just as they were justified in doing in the previous cycle.

Now I am in a position to state my objection to the endeavour of grounding the significance of determinism on cyclicity. It is generally agreed that determinism may be of at least two kinds: one, according to which the past determines the future and also the future the past, and another according to which only the first condition obtains. (According to the second, weaker doctrine, determinism is asymmetrical with respect to time, and, while given a set of physical conditions another unique set will inevitably follow, it is not determined which set of conditions must precede it.) It would seem quite absurd to argue that, although the claim that the universe is deterministic in the stronger sense is legitimate, the other, or weaker, claim is devoid of empirical significance. But the present considerations would commit us to the view that two-way determinism is empirically significant, since it entails the confirmable statement 'If the universe is in identical states more than once, it goes through ever-recurring cycles both in the past and in the future', whereas one-way determinism implies nothing confirmable.

The force of this argument may not be evident at once and some might be tempted to resist it by saying that the confirmability of one-way determinism is guaranteed by the confirmability of two-way determinism. It is agreed, after all, that any expression conveying an empirical falsehood has cognitive significance, and that if the universe is governed by two-way determinism then it is not governed by one-way determinism. Thus to whatever degree two-way determinism receives confirmation, and hence credibility, the claim that the universe is governed by one-way determinism receives disconfirmation to exactly the same degree, and the significance of the claim is thereby assured.

However, this argument is based on a serious error. Suppose it is claimed that in addition to all the colours perceived by us there also exists a colour very dissimilar to any of them (let us call it i-colour) which is imperceptible to us but perceptible to beings with whom men necessarily cannot communicate. It would then be vacuous to attribute i-colour to surfaces. Yet on the assumption that no surface can have two different colours simultaneously, given that object O is red, it follows that O is not i-coloured; hence the sentence 'O is i-coloured' is false and therefore cognitively meaningful. The argument is of the following form:

(1) $(f)(g)(fO.(f \neq g) \supset \sim gO$ (where 'f' and 'g' are variables ranging over all colours)

(2) rO

(3) $\sim iO$

and the error is easily exposed by pointing out that (3) follows only if 'i' is an admissible constant and that since 'g' ranges over colours only, and 'i' has not yet been established to denote a colour, we do not obtain (3) unless we already presuppose it.

Similarly here we have (writing D_1 and D_2 for one-way and two-way determinism respectively):

(1) $(f)(g)(fU.(f \neq g) \supset \sim gU$ (where 'f' and 'g' are variables ranging over all the possible exclusive structures the universe may have)

(2) $D_2 U$ (which we establish through the fact that the universe goes through infinite identical cycles)

(3) $\sim D_1 U$

which is fallacious since we first have to establish that D_1 stands for an admissible structure before we may substitute it for 'g'

(3) *Scientific and Meta-Scientific Statements*

It appears to me that it has to be admitted that no particular event is required or is precluded by the statement that the world is strictly deterministic. On the other hand, it seems clear that the doctrine of determinism is entailed by a particular proposition, which is itself a typical meta-scientific statement since it implies many observations not of how the world is but of how science is. Consider:

> P: S specifies all the relevant initial conditions and provides all the laws required to make the necessary computations which jointly yield a correct answer to any question of the form, 'What observable situation obtains at such-and-such a place and at such-and-such a time?'

(Note: S is a variable for which we may substitute the set of statements constituting science at any given time.) P obviously entails determinism.

Is P confirmable? P is certainly falsifiable—more so than any other statement: every observation statement is a potential falsifier of P. But, according to our criterion, this is not what confers empirical significance upon statements. Now P clearly says something different from any of the statements constituting science; it is a meta-scientific statement making an assertion about the power of the system of statements constituting science taken as a whole. No such assertion—namely, that science is complete, which of course may be observed whether true or false—is made by any intra-scientific statement. If science were to reach that state of perfection in which everything is predictable and no phenomenon is left unaccounted for, in other words if P were no longer falsified, then, while every observation we made would be accounted for by a member of S, the observation *that* every observation we made was accounted for by a member of S would not be asserted by any member of S. P

however asserts just that, namely, that no observation is ever made which is not accounted for by S. In other words, S accounts for first-order observations, i.e. for natural phenomena, while P makes an assertion about S implying second order observations, namely, the observation that S is successful in assigning the right event to any space-time co-ordinate. Consequently, we have succeeded in describing a situation—the situation in which science reaches its ultimate perfection—where P is verified. P entails determinism. Thus there is a conceivable situation in which determinism is verified. Determinism is verifiable and empirically significant.

It might seem that through a similar approach indeterminism could be shown to be confirmed under certain circumstances. For let Q stand for 'Nothing more is predictable about the movement of bodies than what can be predicted on the basis of Newtonian mechanics'. Suppose Q is asserted in the seventeenth century after the spectacular successes of Newtonian mechanics, but when nothing is known about the nature of electricity. On rainy days when some bodies collect large amounts of static electricity, not only is it impossible to predict the way they will act upon each other, but it can be shown that their movements are in principle unpredictable on the basis of Newtonian mechanics (since, while their masses remain constant and the distance separating them unaltered, the force between them may undergo change).

The following now appears true:

(1) Q implies indeterminism—since there are motions which are unpredictable on the basis of Newtonian mechanics.

(2) Q is confirmed as long as Newton's mechanics is not superseded or is not supplemented by a new theory.

I believe that (2) is undisputably true. (1), however, may be questioned. The term 'predictable' may be construed in two different ways resulting in two versions of Q, Q_1 and Q_2. In the former, 'predictable' is spelled out as 'predictable in practice'; in the latter, as 'predictable in principle'. Q_2, of course, implies indeterminism but it is not confirmed relative to Q_1. But the two competing versions of Q imply exactly the same observations, namely, that we always fail to account for the motions which are unaccountable on the basis of Newtonian mechanics. Q_2, although it says more than

Q_1 does, still yields no further observation than what follows from Q_1, and is not therefore the acceptable version of Q. Indeterminism is not confirmed relative to the accepted hypothesis and cannot therefore be said to be supported by the findings of contemporary physics.

Of course, P also has two parallel versions: P_1 and P_2. In P_1, S is actually specified, while P_2 asserts merely that there is some yet unspecified (and possibly in practice never specifiable) S, which lays down all the relevant conditions and provides all the laws, etc. There are a number of asymmetries between P and Q. In the case of P, it is P_1 which makes the stronger claim; P_2, in fact, does not entail the predictability in practice of any observation. Yet even P_2, the weaker assertion, implies that the universe is deterministic. These asymmetries follow from the essential differences between determinism and indeterminism. Complete predictability in practice entails determinism but is not entailed by it; nonpredictability in practice, on the other hand, does not entail indeterminism although it is entailed by it. Because of these basic differences, it seems to follow that circumstances are describable in which determinism would, on the basis of the Universal criterion of confirmation, be regarded as confirmed. No circumstances seem to exist which would render indeterminism confirmed. No circumstances seem to exist which would render indeterminism confirmable.

(4) *The Status of Assertions that Something is Impossible*

Now we reach the crucial stage in our discussion, where the fundamental difference between the doctrine of determinism and its denial, on the one hand, and ordinary intra-scientific statements, on the other hand, breaks through the surface. In general, it will be admitted that when T_1 and T_2 account for precisely the same set of observations and the postulates of T_1 form a proper subset of the postulates of T_2, then we prefer T_1 which has no redundant elements. The situation with respect to Q_1 and Q_2 may, however, be said not to be strictly like that. The extra elements in Q_2 are not entirely redundant: they explain Q_1. If we opt for Q_2 alone, then we have no explanation why it is that we cannot discover any laws accounting for forces unaccounted for in Newtonian mechancis.

Q_2, however, provides an excellent explanation: there are no such laws.

This, however, may be countered by saying that Q_2 is not the only possible explanation for our failure completely to account for all the forces with which bodies interact. It may be that masses never partake in any motion which is not law-governed and hence in principle unpredictable, but that some of the laws governing the movements of bodies are too elusive for us to discover.

Ultimately, then, the problem facing us is which is the preferable explanation for the fact that certain movements are unpredictable in practice: that they are unpredictable in principle or that the laws required for their prediction are sufficiently difficult to have escaped us so far? Whatever we may think of the relative merits of these two explanations—as long as the laws of electricity are not discovered—no empirical discoveries of any sort can be expected to have great effect in changing our opinion. Unlike the case of conflicting scientific hypotheses of comparable merit, here we cannot count on the intervention of that universal process whereby sooner or later the ground is relentlessly shifted—through the combined effects of new discoveries made in different areas of natural phenonema—in favour of the hypothesis eventually to be accepted by all.

When the Michelson-Morley experiment had failed to disclose the absolute motion of the earth, it was possible to suggest that none of the experiments in the past designed for the purpose had disclosed the motion of the earth through space because, in fact, such motion did not exist, and it was also possible to say that absolute velocity as well as relative velocity is real except that so far we have not hit upon the right experiment through which the former may be detected. On the surface, the question, whether to attribute Newton's failure to discover all the laws of motion to a lack of good fortune and ingenuity or to the non-existence of such laws, may seem very similar to the question how best to interpret Michelson and Morley's failure to discover our motion through the aether. But the two situations are fundamentally dissimilar: for the first is a meta-scientific question the answer to which must be based on observing science, what laws it can and what laws it cannot produce, while the other is a scientific question to be answered through observing natural phenomena that are innumerably many and are throughly intermeshed.

Whenever the correct answer to the first question is that the generation of certain forces is unpredictable in principle or in practice only, no matter how many more facts we discover, or to what extent our theories expand and our knowledge advances, it will never make more than a single practical difference. If there are no laws governing these forces, then we shall never discover them, and if such laws do exist then eventually we might actually do so. It seems impossible to conceive of any new discovery which could considerably change the situation with respect to this question, except one: the discovery of the laws on the basis of which movements unaccounted for by Newton, are predictable.

Not so in the case of the second question. Science is infinitely rich while meta-science consists of precious few sentences. There are infinitely many statements about natural phenomena, each interconnected with innumerable others, but one can think of very few statements that are like the statement about universal determinism, i.e. which are second-order observation statements in the sense that they are directly affected by any first-order observation. Given the fact that statements describing nature form a vast intermeshed system, innumerable differences hinge upon the question as to which is the correct explanation for the consistent failure to determine our speed through the aether. By adopting the correct explanation, we shall be able to predict a large number of natural phenomena, the existence of which would otherwise have to be independently assumed. As is well known, the non-existence of absolute motion is turned, in contemporary physics, into a constructive principle called the principle of relativity, which, in conjunction with a number of other postulates, implies an indefinite number of various other observable facts (e.g. the Mössbauer effect). These phenomena, therefore, may all be construed as positive evidence that absolute motion does not exist. No such evidence could be forthcoming to support the thesis that the movements of bodies are in principle unaccountable. It does not seem possible that the meta-scientific hypothesis, that some motions of bodies occur at random and are undetermined by the initial conditions, should by itself or in conjunction with other hypotheses give rise to predictions (except, of course, the one and only prediction that some movements will for ever remain unpredictable).

Similarly, suppose it were said: quantum mechanics can be shown to be incapable of predicting certain micro-occurances. Eventually, however, an entirely new science may arise, introducing undreamed-of new parameters on the basis of which all micro-events become predictable. The denial of this claim would amount to the meta-scientific assertion that the world is indeterministic; it would not and it could not by itslef, or in combination with other statements, imply any predictions other than that certain micro-events will for ever remain unaccounted for. Contrast this, however, with the assertion about the impossibility of constructing a perpetual-motion machine. Originally this assertion was prompted by the persistent failure of the most ingenious efforts to construct such a machine. But the assertion is an intra-scientific one; consequently it implies much more than just that we shall never succeed in building a perpetual-motion machine. As we know, the assertion has been employed as a positive principle known as the First Law of Thermodynamics which, in conjunction with a number of other established postulates, has all sorts of factual implications.

The question whether our failure to construct a perpetual-motion machine is due to our lacking the required ingenuity or to the fact that such a machine is in principle impossible, becomes more and more positively answered with the increasing range of success of thermodynamics. This dispute, which takes place within science, is eventually settled. The dispute, over whether the failure of science to account for certain phenomena should be attributed to the lack of required ingenuity on the part of scientists or to the fact that events are in principle unaccountable for, may, on the other hand, for ever remain unsettled.

Finally, let us for a brief moment consider the claim commonly made in the nineteenth century that, from the state of science at the time, one was to conclude that the world was strictly deterministic. The claim was prompted by the enormous success of the scientific enterprise in finding causes for all sorts of events and it was advanced in spite of the realization that there were still many phenomena unaccounted-for and that science had not reached a state of perfection.

Again, it seems that there are no decisive arguments to show that this meta-scientific claim was at the time incorrectly advanced. For let '*C*' stand for 'Every event has a cause' or 'Every event occurs in accordance with some law of nature'. It may be argued that '*C*' is similar to a statement like 'All ravens are black': the latter entails that if i is a raven then i is black and is confirmed by the observation that i is both a raven and black; it also entails that if j is a raven then j is black and is neither confirmed nor disconfirmed when we observe j to be a raven but are prevented from finding out whether or not j is black. For, in the case of *C*, we should argue that it entails that, if e is an event, e has a cause or e occurs in accordance with some law of nature; and hence the discovery of the law of nature, in accordance with which e occurs, confirms *C*. On the other hand, *C* is neither confirmed nor disconfirmed when we come across e^1, which is an event, and do not succeed in discovering a law in accordance with which it occurred, which after all does not amount to finding that e^1 occurred in accordance with no law.

This argument could be countered by pointing out that the two cases are not quite similar. In the case of the ravens, some specific obstacle prevented us from observing the colour of a given raven. In the other case, however, free of all impediment, we explored every avenue we could think of, still failing to come up with a cause. But, as we have already seen, whether a persistent failure to come up with a law of nature governing certain phenomena should be construed as evidence that none exists is not the type of question which can be decisively settled.

Index